POTTERY COTTAGE

ALAN HURNDALL is an award-winning journalist and film maker working in newspapers and television. He is a former Campaigning Journalist of the Year, a BAFTA nominee, and a Royal Television Society winner. He was a lecturer in journalism and media law at Sheffield Hallam University and holds a Masters Degree in Creative Writing. He lives in Derbyshire, not far from Pottery Cottage.

As a news reporter on The Star, Sheffield in the mid 70s, he worked on the Pottery Cottage story. Using the Freedom of Information Act he applied to Derbyshire Police for documentation about the case. He is hugely indebted to the Force for their help.

Pottery Cottage is his second non-fiction book.

'Alan is a master storyteller. I couldn't put this down.'
David Mastin, newspaper executive.

'I thought I knew this story.. but within a few pages I realised I didn't.'
Jim Raven, author.

By the same author

NON FICTION
The Invisible Girl

POTTERY COTTAGE

ALAN HURNDALL

The following is a true story which happened in the Peak District of Derbyshire, England in 1977. It is based on a record of actual events, the testimonies of people involved, official reports, transcripts of proceedings, witnesses at the time, police files, newspaper cuttings, and interviews carried out by the author.

Dialogue has been recorded from the recollections of people who were there and from statements to police. Some aspects of dialogue, although based on actual conversations, have been devised for the purpose of continuity, understanding and dramatic effect.

WEDNESDAY

7am

January 12th 1977.

The Peak District, Derbyshire, England.

In the upstairs master bedroom of Pottery Cottage, an alarm clock rang out and a woman's hand reached across to kill it with a thud. Gill Moran grabbed her gown, pulled back the curtains and peered out into the darkness. 'Oh, my goodness!'

A lone car navigated the moorland road, its headlights spotlighting falling snow. On the drive, Richard's car was wrapped in a white blanket.

She gave him a nudge. 'You'll need to clear the drive.'

Their home stood at the gateway of the Peak District, Britain's first National Park, mile upon mile of rolling moorland, craggy hills and gentle valleys.

They lived in Eastmoor, a ribbon of cottages, farms and a couple of pubs, sandwiched between the working-class market town of Chesterfield to the east, and the aristocratic Chatsworth Estate a few miles west.

Pottery was once the backbone of the local economy but the wheels had stopped turning long ago and the little gritstone factory converted into four dwellings.

To the rear, beyond the farmland, and dry-stone walls, the moors stretched as far as the eye could see. The ever-changing colours charted the calendar – the green shoots of spring, the parched brown of summer, misty autumn golds, and, on this winter's dawn, a cold, leaden grey.

That was just about it. Their community. Little had changed for years and they preferred it that way.

Downstairs, Gill filled the kettle and switched on the radio. *The north of England is bracing itself for one of the worst winter storms for years with two days of heavy snow forecast.'*

Summer had been so lovely, a record heatwave. Now it was payback time.

She let the dogs in - Emma, their fussy basset hound, and nosey old Labrador Willie - knocking over their food bowls in the race to the fridge.

Richard Moran entered in his bathrobe. He was sales director and partner of a plastics company half an hour away, but today had a business meeting in Birmingham.

'Two hundred miles in this! Are you really sure, Richard? Maybe you can put them off. I'm sure they'd understand.'

'I've told you a million times not to exaggerate,' he said. He was a master of deflecting obstacles with a jolly quip. He waited a beat for the joke to sink in.

'It's eighty, tops. Besides, I'm paying for lunch. They'll think me a real eejit. With a bit of luck, I'll seal the deal,' he said.

His soft Irish accent was always reassuring. Anyway, he was rather looking forward to the journey, regarding the weather more as a challenge than a hindrance.

They were still on a post-Christmas weekday regime of starch-reduced crispbread. Most days they breakfasted together – their only guaranteed catch-up time to chat, sort household and family matters, and discuss social events. Today it would be a couple of snatched Ryvitas.

'What time you back?' Gill asked.

'Sixish. You know what these things are like. If it gets too heavy I'll have to have a kip in the car before driving back,' he said.

'All right for some,' she said.

She went to the fridge for some juice which she poured into Sarah's pink beaker – the only colour her daughter would drink from.

Sarah's kingdom was behind a latchkey door decorated with a badge of Black Beauty and a sticker of the Womble Uncle Bulgaria. And, in case of doubt, a ceramic sign proclaimed 'Sarah's Room.'

Inside was like Dr Who's Tardis – a school desk, two cupboards which weren't enough for her pot-pourri of toys, games and dolls; a wardrobe, rocking horse, and a bedside table where her National Cycling Proficiency certificate was proudly framed next to a tinkling musical box crammed with trinkets and jewellery.

She slept in a sea of pink, surrounded by soft toys and clutching Jumbo, her elephant comforter. Her bed was guarded when she was out by a giant-sized teddy that Santa had brought one Christmas.

From the window – still decorated with Christmas paper-chains - she could keep an eye on the constant scraps in the yard between the dogs and her cat Ginger, with Bo-Bo, her rabbit, a fascinated spectator from the safety of his hutch in the corner.

Most days the ten-year-old woke early, hovering behind the door waiting for the creak of the staircase, then leaping back under the covers pretending to be asleep. Gill would sit patiently on the bed gently coaxing her to wake up.

'Tell you what, if you get up before I count to five, I'll give you a lift to school instead of you having to wait in the cold for the bus. How about that?'

Gill began counting. At 'three' Sarah sprang from under the sheets with a beaming smile.

Sarah got herself ready and was soon downstairs in her grey school tunic, white blouse and green school sweater.

Her gran, Amy Minton, appeared from the adjoining kitchen, grandad Arthur limping behind on his false leg.

The Mintons lived in half of Pottery Cottage. A sliding door linked the two households. It was an ideal arrangement - one big family with unbridled access, but each with their own space.

'What a day!' said Amy. 'Make sure you wrap up nice and warm, Sarah.' She was holding Sarah's winter coat. It was only the start of the negotiations. 'I'm not wearing that,' she said.

Arthur piped in. 'You'll learn one day my love that nanna is ALWAYS right.'

'Have you fed Bo-Bo?' said Amy. Sarah slipped the coat on to go outside. Amy winked at Arthur at her little victory.

Richard came in from outside carrying a shovel dripping with snow. Under his shabby garden coat was a smart business suit.

'Right then, all systems go.'

Sarah ran to him for a hug and a kiss. 'Be good. See you tonight. Emil and the Detectives, yeah!'

Gill came down made up and wearing trousers, a green Simon shirt, and expensive fine-wool jumper. Richard pecked her on the cheek. 'None of your Stirling Moss antics,' she said.

He gave a mock salute, clicked his heels military-style, and disappeared out the door. Within two minutes he was back inside muttering that the car wouldn't start. He fretted from room to room obviously looking for something and then disappeared outside.

From the lounge window, Gill watched him fiddle inside the bonnet, slam the lid, and get back in the car. The Chrysler 180 sprang into life. He punched the air and pulled out. With luck, in half an hour or so he would be on the M1 heading south.

7.05am that day.

Leicester Prison, England.

Competing with the din of clanging metal, slopping out, and jangling keys, a remand prisoner made a call on the landing pay-phone. Behind him, two inmates waited in line. A screw hovered a few feet away.

It was answered in the bedroom of a terraced house in Chesterfield fifty-five miles to the north. The ringing jolted Teressa O'Doherty awake. *Who the bloody hell's this?*

She reached for the phone. A whisper came down the line.

'No-one with you, I hope.'

'Shit, Billy. How'd you get my number?'

'The Directory Enquiries lady was very helpful. She even gave me your new address. Derby Road, eh!. I wondered why you hadn't answered my letters.'

Tess's heart skipped a beat.

'I've told you before, Tess, if you ever left me or let me down, there would only be one person I'd come after. There'd be no getting away. I would find out where you lived.'

Tess said nothing. She was shaking, struggling to hold the receiver steady against her ear.

'I need a favour, babe,' he said.

Despite his threats she was determined to stay strong.

'It's over. Do you want me to spell it out? O.V.E.R!'

But he was persistent. 'My trial's today, Tess. Chesterfield. I need you to put a word in.'

'... Oh, yes, M'lud. This man's not what you think. He's a saint in disguise.'

Billy interrupted – 'please, Tess. Just tell the judge you're standing by me. I'll make it up to you, I swear.'

'Do yourself a favour, Billy. Serve your time and then go back to your wife and kid.'

'I'm facing a ten! You're all I've got in the world.'

'Sorry, Billy. It's a workday.'

She hung up.

Billy exploded at the dead receiver, banging it against the wall. 'You fucking bitch. you'd better lock your fucking doors.'

Subliminal images invaded his head. He was slitting her throat, the blood spurting out like a fountain. She was begging for mercy. He merely smiled and gave her some more.

The waiting cons looked down at the floor. The screw allowed him a moment then moved in and ushered him away.

Tess turned on the bedside light. She lay in bed staring at the ceiling, shaking. She lit a cigarette, a hundred different thoughts going through her head.

Two minutes after that call, prisoner 18043 was back in the heat of the kitchen washing piles of pots and bowls. He was down to his sleeveless vest, showcasing his bulging biceps and edgy tattoos of snakes and naked female bodies. He was on auto-pilot. He couldn't get Tess out of his mind. *The bitch. She deserves what's coming to her.*

The supervisor arrived from the main hall where there'd been an altercation between two inmates. He kept a tight ship, but had a soft spot for Billy who appeared to be a hard worker who kept his nose clean. Some even speculated that the screw's interest in the rugged, good-looking prisoner was more than professional. How else could a long-term criminal with a record of violence be put in the kitchen surrounded by potentially lethal weapons?

'Love your enemies, do good to them, then your reward will be great. You believe in the Good Lord, son?'

As with all screws, Billy hated the bastard and just strung him along.

'Still waiting for the sign, guv.'

'Ah, never give up. There's hope for us all, you know!'

'I shared a cell with a bible basher once. Praise ye the Lord, morning, noon and bloody night,' said Billy, his arms groping in the dirty water.

'Did he find peace?'

'We both did… he topped himself.'

Billy pulled the plug, his work for the day over. They watched the water drain away. The screw nodded approval. 'They found him hanging from the rafters in the prison chapel. He'd cut up the priest's tunic and knotted the pieces together. Ironic, eh?'

Again, Billy pictured himself looking up the body of his cellmate swinging from the chapel rafters. 'Mind if I slope off now, boss, only I've got court and need to get ready and that.' Billy raised his arms for the obligatory frisking. Their eyes met close.

'That story,' said the screw, suspicion in his eye, 'a load of bullshit and we both know it.'

Billy walked off to go to his cell, sensing the supervisor's eyes on his arse all the way to the door.

-3-

7.45am

Leicester city centre

In his pokey little base, David Reynolds made himself a coffee and began reading the paper, wondering what the day would hold. He was the proprietor of Highfields Taxis, sited in the old weighbridge toll office in the centre of Leicester.

He was only 34, but had scrimped and saved to start his own business and got lucky when the Gothic-style building became available. It was perfectly situated - on a little island between the old tram tracks - with ample parking for his small fleet of cars. Trade was good. The base was ideal for shoppers during the day, and the Palais and cinemagoers at nights and weekends.

He'd recently made it onto the approved list of taxi firms at Leicester Prison, providing a lucrative if infrequent income, transporting staff and prisoners here there and everywhere. And so it was to be this very day. A chance fare.

Shortly before eight, the phone rang. It was the plaintive voice of a woman in the admin office at the jail. Sorry for the short notice, but

could a taxi be at the prison in ten minutes to do a detail to
Chesterfield?

It was chaos, she said, trying to cope with the first cold snap of
winter. They had a duty to despatch dozens of inmates to courts and
institutions around the country. But today the weather meant delays,
cancellations and breakdowns through minor bumps and flat batteries.

There weren't enough minibuses to transfer prisoners to court. It
meant that local taxi companies were needed to take up the slack.

'It's all straightforward, a remand prisoner being escorted to court.
Just drop the escort party at the courthouse. You'll be back by mid-
morning,' she said.

Reynolds had done seven prison escorts before, but had never been
to Chesterfield. He grabbed his puffa jacket and keys to his Persian-
blue Morris 1800.

The prison was only five minutes away. He reported at the gate, and
joined the line of vehicles pumping petrol and diesel fumes waiting for
their passengers to appear.

The prison was built to resemble a castle with a brief to make it
look as fearsome as possible as a 'deterrent to the masses.' On this
winter morn at least, the design worked perfectly. In daylight, the
exterior was a distinctive red brick, but in this pre-dawn darkness it
formed an irregular, almost spooky silhouette. Sleet drove against the
turrets and portcullis, and dripped from the barbed wire down the walls
- the highest of any jail in Britain.

Reynolds waited while fiddling with his radio and heater controls,
keeping an eye on the door for his escort party to emerge. After ten
minutes they hadn't shown. He turned the engine off and began filling
in his TV licence renewal form.

Pottery Cottage

Gill and Sarah were ready to leave. Sarah had decided she would in fact wear her winter coat and fretted in the hall, swinging her lunchbox waiting for her mother. 'Give nanna a kiss,' said Amy.

'And I want a big one,' said Arthur, before disappearing next door.

Gill came down in fur boots and a camel coat and holding a carrier bag containing her office shoes and Ryvita lunch. 'I'll ring later about tea, mum.'

Amy rushed to the kitchen as if she'd forgotten something. She emerged with a woollen bobble-hat matching Sarah's red coat. She pulled it down on Sarah's head. In the drive, Sarah waited for Amy to close the door behind them before tearing it off.

'She can't make me!' said Sarah. Gill shook her head.

Wigley Primary School was five minutes up the road.

'What have you got on today?' Gill asked.

'Not much.'

Sometimes Sarah could chat for England. She was hyperactive, full of beans and spirit. But today wasn't one of those days. Who knew what went on in that mind? Gill didn't.

On the approach, a line of red tail-lights stretched back a hundred yards or so. The pavement was a sea of umbrellas and coats over heads. The sun was now up, but you wouldn't know. The 80-year-old stone schoolhouse was submerged in the fog of fumes as cars dropped off their young ones or manoeuvred to park on the icy verges.

'I'll take you in,' said Gill.

'No, I want to go by myself,' Sarah replied.

'Okay, but go straight in… and be careful on the pavement, it's very slippery.'

Sarah was straight out of the car, slamming the door, and off down the footpath without saying a word. Gill watched the little girl disappear, her long blonde hair now speckled with snow.

Back in the cottage, Amy had cleared away the breakfast things in both kitchens. Arthur peered out at the gloom. 'I were going into town, but not in this,' he said.

Amy had a better idea. 'I'll tell you what, why don't we get a fire going and I'll make us some soup for lunch?'

With that, Arthur put his work coat on and retired to the garage to chop wood.

Back in his cell, Billy's heart was pumping. He was stripped down to his underpants, his prison greys in a heap on the floor. One of the screws assigned to escort him to court was waiting the other side of the half-open door but Billy's thoughts were a long way from answering to justice.

He glanced back over his shoulder. All clear. He lifted the corner of the bed mattress and scoured the underside until he located a small slit. For a muscular man, he had unusually small hands - small enough to squeeze inside that tiny opening. His hand was shaking. He took a deep breath.

He navigated the rusty springs and tightly-packed bedding material. Then he found it – a seven-inch boning knife. He wrapped it in toilet paper and tucked it down the front of his Y Fronts. 'Be there in a jiffy, boss. Just putting me strides on,' he shouted.

The screw was Ken Simmonds, 41, a former lorry-driver and amateur boxer, in his third year as a prison officer. He wasn't to know, but his patience in the last two minutes probably saved his life.

With the weapon now safely tucked away, Billy wondered what he'd have done if the screw had come in and caught him with the knife. He would have used it on him, that's for sure, straight through the throat probably. To hell with the consequences, nothing was going to get in his way.

'Just the shoes now boss, and that'll be it,' he barked at the door.

He fast-changed into his only suit – a thin summer navy pinstripe, worn over a blue open-necked floral shirt, and a white silk waistcoat - and checked his hair in the hand mirror.

He took a last lingering look around the cell - bunk bed, table, chair, picture board, small cupboard, Playboy mags, and shaving stuff. On the floor was his slop bucket, discarded uniform, and a shattered picture frame that up until a few minutes ago carried a photo of Tess. The picture was now in shreds. He allowed himself one brief private smirk. A final goodbye. 'Ready boss, let's go,' he said.

It took two minutes to walk down to reception, Simmonds puffing behind in his gabardine coat over his uniform. He strode confidently, glancing up at the rafters. From his pace, no-one could possibly imagine he had a seven-inch blade digging into his bollocks.

A cry of 'good luck Billy boy' rang out anonymously from behind a cell door. No one particularly liked him, but they feared him, that was for sure. Besides, every con supported a brother on his way to court.

The two cellblocks, each with four landings, were evil twins, everything identical - the floors, the cells, smells, sounds, the florescent lighting, even the placement of the switches. They'd tried to brighten the place up, every so often re-painting those ancient walls - magnolia, red and orange - but a lick of paint could never brush away the stench and hopelessness of incarceration.

The only sense of the outside world in the cellblock was in daylight when the sun shone through the glass ceiling, sending down square patterns of light where the iron bars criss-crossed the girders.

He'd had taken that route many times in recent weeks – along the lino floor, down the central staircase, through the security doors and into the linking corridor to reception. At the green-painted reception area, the despatch officer looked up from his desk. 'Ah, Ken, there you are. You're with Don Sprintall. He's just sorting the paperwork.'

Sprintall arrived a few moments later. He was 46, over 6ft, with a frame to match, balding, with long sideburns. He was old school, immaculately dressed, with polished shoes and buttons. He was holding a briefcase containing, amongst other things, booklet 331 – the standing instructions to be carried by lead officers conducting escorts.

Fourteen years a prison officer, Sprintall knew those instructions by heart, but it was compulsory to carry the booklet and he was a stickler for protocol.

Booklet 331 underlined the most obvious rule of all - that the first duty of the officer in charge was to ensure that the prisoner did not escape. All prisoners must be thoroughly searched, and he must examine the handcuffs before leaving the prison to satisfy himself that all was in order. Sprintall whispered to the duty deskman. 'Any history?'

'None that I'm aware. Straightforward remand, I guess. He's usually as good as gold,' said the deskman.

'What's his name?' 'Hughes. Billy Hughes.' Sprintall shrugged. Neither escort had had dealings with Hughes before. Just another day, just another prisoner. 'Right', said Sprintall, 'a closet chain and then we're sorted.'

'Sorry, they're all out,' said the deskman.

'But they're standard issue.'

'I suggest you take it up with the powers that be.'

Sprintall turned to Hughes – 'You can either use the toilet now or wait till we get to court. Your choice.'

Billy said nothing. The only thing that mattered was getting through the rub-down. The last thing he wanted was to risk having a piss. Simmonds stepped forward and beckoned. 'Right son, you know the score.'

This was it. The moment of truth. Billy put his hands in the air and focussed on a single brick in the wall. He stood like a statue, anxious not to provoke any suspicion or a break in routine. He'd been searched this way scores of times in his life. But this was the most important, a gamble that they would follow the usual perfunctory search.

Never were the stakes so high. If they found the knife now, his chance of escape would be over. All that careful planning down the fucking drain over one busybody screw.

'You all right, Hughes? You're usually full of chunter. Cat got your tongue?' The deskman was trying to goad him. The usual shit. *Fuck you*, Billy thought. Then suddenly, Simmonds broke off. An unexpected delay. *What the fuck's wrong?* 'Remove your jacket,' he ordered. Billy nervously obeyed.

Simmonds frisked the top of his shoulders, then underneath his arms and down the front and back of his shirt and waistcoat. Billy daren't even flinch. The screw then scoured his ankles, and went up the outside of the trousers. He was now just a few inches from the knife. At what point would he stop?

Billy remained deadpan, staring at the wall. His mouth was dry. He licked his lips. He was banking on the fear all screws had of accidentally touching the private parts during a search and risk accusations of sexual assault. Simmonds stopped abruptly and looked at his colleagues.

'Okay, we're ready.'

Billy held his wrists out to be cuffed. He looked up to the heavens. He couldn't believe his luck. He could feel the blade against his skin. Yes, it was there! *Sweet.*

Outside, Reynolds saw the outline of three matchstick men exit the building. He flashed his headlights. They acknowledged with a wave. He pulled up so they wouldn't have to walk through the sleet.

The screw with handcuffs on got in the back and slid across to allow his prisoner room to sit beside him. The other walked the few yards to the gatehouse where he collected some forms. After a minute he returned and got in the front.

'Okay, Ken. Check the cuffs and we'll get on our way,' said Sprintall. 'Secure,' he replied. Sprintall turned towards Reynolds.

'Right, a few things to go through. We stick to the route map unless I say. You obviously don't need me to tell you to observe the speed limits at all times. I don't know how many escorts you've done, but I'm not permitted to allow anyone to have a conversation with the prisoner during the journey, and that of course includes you. And I'd prefer it if the radio was turned off … too much of a distraction, but we'll see how we go.'

Reynolds obliged. He looked in the rear-view mirror ready to pull away. The prisoner beamed back at him. Reynolds wasn't sure whether to acknowledge him or not. He offered a cursory smile back. Reynolds wondered what the man had done. Was he a thief, a conman, fraudster, sex offender? His crime couldn't be that serious, or they'd have used a prison vehicle, he thought.

And so they set off - two prison officers doing their duty on a supposedly routine escort, a taxi proprietor who'd won a chance fare because of the weather, and a ruthless inmate concealing a lethal weapon on a mission to escape.

Reynolds turned left, out through the suburbs to the dual A50. It would be 15 minutes to the M1, then north for 45 miles until junction 29. From there Chesterfield was five miles by dual carriageway.

Progress was slow – the usual mix of lorries, reps on their way to meetings, parents on the school run, people travelling to work. All with their headlights and wipers on. Reynolds settled into the inside lane doing around 60 mph. No-one spoke. Simmonds tried to get something going about fishing, but his colleague had his head buried in paperwork, and dipping in and out of his briefcase.

Reynolds concentrated on the road. Lorries threw up plumes of spray making conditions testing. Hughes watched the sleet dribble down the outside of his window. Every so often he rubbed the condensation with his sleeve, trying to work out exactly where they were. On the M1, four junctions from their turnoff, Billy noticed the sign for 'services.' He rolled down the window. The rush of cold, noisy air startled the others.

'What do you think you're doing?' It was Simmonds next to him.

'I need some air, boss,' said Hughes. 'Close it,' said Simmonds.

Hughes reluctantly wound the window back up.

'I need to go to the toilet.'

'No way. You had your chance at the nick. Besides, we're running late as it is.'

Hughes opened the window again, this time theatrically clutching his stomach and putting his mouth to the gap, gasping for air. 'I'm desperate!' Simmonds was getting frustrated. 'We're only half an hour from the courthouse. You'll just have to hold on.'

Hughes notched up the pressure. 'Fine, but don't blame me if I shit all over the car.'

Reynolds was horrified. 'There's a service station up here, if that's any good.' Sprintall threw him a look which said mind your own business. Hughes sensed a split. 'It must be something I've eaten. Please boss, it's nearly coming out. I can't appear in court having shat myself...'

Reynolds was onside. He turned to Sprintall. 'Any mess and you'll have to have it valeted and compensate me for time off the road.'

A prison escort was never happy about stopping. There was always a risk that a prisoner had set something up, or that he would flee in the crowd, maybe hijack a car. Then there were the busybodies. Seeing a man in handcuffs attracted unwanted attention. They also didn't have closet chains – handcuffs with extra-long chains specifically designed for when prisoners use the lavatory in a public place.

'You heard what I said,' said Sprintall.

Hughes snapped back. 'I know my rights. I'm gonna complain to the judge.'

23

Sprintall pondered for a moment. Sure, the system would back him, but did he need the aggro? And what if the bastard <u>did</u> mess the car! 'I could do with stretching my legs... Ken, you fancy some fresh air?' His partner got the message.' I 'spose it is a bit stuffy in here,' said Simmonds.

Sprintall nodded to Reynolds who moved to the outside lane and put his foot down.

Trowell Services, between Junctions 25 and 26 of the M1 in Nottinghamshire, shone like a beacon in the gloom. Motorway service stations were refuges only for the desperate. And after his Oscar-winning performance in the back seat, Hughes certainly seemed exactly that.

When it opened in 1967, they'd intended to make Trowell a 'go-to' destination. Situated on the edge of Sherwood Forest, they gave it a Robin Hood theme. It was full of medieval pastiche – heraldic decorations, mosaic jousting knights, and 'the world-famous Sheriff's Restaurant.' It was a marketing fantasy. The reality, like nearly all such establishments, was soggy chips, congealed food and petrol at rip-off prices.

Reynolds drove into the main car-park with a sense of urgency and pulled up side-on to the cafeteria building, a low-slung affair of peeling paint adorned by advertising boards and on this murky day, glaring neon lights. The heavens had granted a five-minute respite from the snow and the place had suddenly become packed with cars and lorries. An outing of sixth-formers scurried for a pee and a bar of chocolate.

Sprintall frowned. He half got out of the car to survey the scene, then held his hand up like the Sheriff of Nottingham.

'Hold your horses. We're not stopping here. It's too busy.'

Hughes groaned and clutched his stomach again.

'You're effing kidding me,' he said.

'Watch it son, we're doing you a favour, remember,' said Simmonds.

Reynolds piped up – 'There's a transport section further in, just for HGVs. It's usually empty. I use it myself sometimes.' 'OK, we'll have a look,' said Sprintall.

Reynolds doubled back so he could park in the section reserved for coaches and heavy goods vehicles. It was indeed much quieter. The only sign of life were two truckers in a lorry cab enjoying a sandwich and a hot drink from a flask.

From the outside, the toilet block looked more like an old village cricket pavilion, drab and isolated, and in need of a lick of paint.

Sprintall went inside alone. It was smelly and dank. There was a single washbasin, cracked mirror and tiles, and a pull-down towel machine.. There was a line of urinals, the floor flooded by pee or water, and six cubicles, their doors open and obviously unoccupied. Importantly, there was no-one around. He hurried back to the taxi.

The three got out and strode purposefully to the block, Hughes still handcuffed to Simmonds. Reynolds stayed in the car with the engine running. He put the radio on, enjoying his five minutes of independence.

Sprintall chose the end cubicle. He stood on the toilet seat and ran his hand over the cistern. The top was covered in rust. Sprintall was satisfied there was no way Hughes could have set anything up. Simmonds unlocked the cuffs. He looked Hughes in the eye.

'Quick as you can. Do exactly as we say, and no funny business. We're the other side of the door. Leave the door unlocked, we'll respect your privacy.' Hughes held his stare. 'Aye, boss,' he said.

He rubbed his hands together to get the blood flowing and went inside, leaving the door ajar as instructed. He hung his jacket on the peg and pulled down his trousers. The parcel inside his pants was warm. He unwrapped it, put the knife in the left pocket of his jacket, and threw the paper down the toilet.

His mission over, he sat on the seat and pretended to defecate, making exaggerated noises of relief. On the other side of the door, the screws exchanged uncomfortable looks. They heard him rip off reams of paper, and flush the toilet several times.

Hughes began whistling a tune and emerged in his waistcoat, his jacket folded across his arm, and with a smile of relief. 'That's better, gentlemen. I can't thank you enough,' he said.

Hughes put his jacket on and held his hands out to be cuffed again. 'Wait,' said Simmonds.

Was the game up? Hughes put his hand in his jacket and clutched the knife.... 'Aren't you going to wash your hands?' Hughes smiled and moved to the sink. They watched him wash and dry his hands and handcuffed him again.

Back in the car, they adopted the same positions. This time, though, the knife was nestling not inside the prisoner's pants ... but in the silk lining of his jacket pocket. And very soon he intended to use it.

9.30am

M1 Motorway, Derbyshire

They'd been back on the motorway for 15 minutes. The blue sign for the Chesterfield turn-off loomed in the windscreen. Hughes waited. And waited. He edged his hand gently towards his jacket pocket. Oh so slowly, he lifted the flap, put his hand inside, and clasped the wooden handle. It felt good. He felt secure, invincible even.

He glanced at the screw next to him. Surely he must have seen what he was up to, or sensed that he was about to make a move? But no. The warden merely stared out of the window in his own little world. In front, the other screw's head was buried in paperwork.

Hughes checked out the motorway. Cars, lorries, coaches, motorbikes, speeding past, wipers and headlights on.

Three hundred yards … two hundred yards… Reynolds indicated to exit. They passed the marker for one hundred yards. The taxi slowed and entered the slip road. It went through the green lights at the roundabout and at the second exit, Reynolds turned onto the dual carriageway signposted 'Chesterfield.'

Hughes could wait no longer. This was his moment, the culmination of everything he'd plotted in those long nights in his cell. It was now or never.

In a fraction of a second, and without a hint of warning, the knife came out of his pocket, through the air and into the neck of Sprintall in front of him, several times, like an axeman chopping wood.

Then, almost in the same movement, he turned the knife on the screw next to him, stabbing him repeatedly about the face and hands.

Years of pent-up fury against the system and his sad pathetic life were released into those poor men.

Simmonds tried to fight back, warding off the blows with his free hand, but the prisoner had surprise, strength, momentum - and of course, a lethal weapon.

Reynolds meanwhile, was paralysed by fear, his hands frozen to the wheel, the vehicle veering across the dual carriageway as he instinctively ducked away from the knifeman's blows.

At first Sprintall thought the taxi had been hit from behind, by a lorry or something. His first reaction was to put his hand to the back of his head. His hair was wet and gooey. There was no pain, but he could feel the strength sap from his body.

The scene in the rear-view mirror was just as gruesome. Reynolds could make out the officer's exposed jaw bone as the blood flowed from an "S" shaped cut.

Sprintall was now slumped in the well of the front seat, groaning. He had a five-inch wound that ran from behind his right ear to the middle of his neck. All Reynolds could do was to toss him a cloth he used to wipe the windscreen.

In that extreme few seconds, Hughes had gained control of the car. It was the sheer speed and ferocity of the attack that made it so successful. He uttered his first command.

'KEEP GOING!'

He was now on top of Simmonds who was pleading, 'no more, no more. You've got me in my jugular. You don't want me to die do you?'

Hughes stood up and reached over the front seat. He put the knife against Sprintall's neck.

'The keys! YOU HEAR? Give me the fucking keys!'

Sprintall just about had the strength to unclick the handcuffs key from his belt and toss it blindly into the back.

Hughes turned to Simmonds. 'Unlock us.'

Simmonds, shaking, and in fear of his life, obliged. Hughes was now free and screaming like a banshee.

'THE BACK... BACK... GET IN THE BACK. DO AS I SAY, GET IN THE BACK.'

Sprintall tried his best. But he just didn't have the capacity. He could only just about get to his feet. The lifeblood was literally draining from him. But Hughes was empowered by adrenaline. He yanked him towards him into the back. Simmonds was about to plead for mercy again but Billy intervened – 'Don't say a fucking word, you hear?'

He handcuffed the men together in one swift movement.

Reynolds eyed the blood-stained seat next to him. And spoke for the first time. 'They need medical attention... they could die. You don't want murder on your hands, do you?'

Hughes was having none of it. 'Just keep your fucking mouth shut and do as I say or you'll be next.'

Hughes leapt in the front and held the tip of the knife into Reynolds' side. He shouted to the back. 'If one of you as much as raises your head, you're both dead meat.'

Reynolds was shaking at the wheel, so scared he was almost unfit to drive. 'Where do you want me to go?'

'How many more times? Just fucking drive!'

At the end of the dual carriageway they approached traffic lights where two lanes expanded into three. They were now in Chesterfield town centre. The lights were on red.

'What now, what now?' Reynolds pleaded.

A woman in a Mini waited at the lights. Reynolds was on course to pull up alongside her.

Hughes' mood changed from chaotic to calm.

'Nice and steady... as if nothing has happened.'

Reynolds stopped beside her. Hughes smiled across, all the while poking the knife against Reynolds' ribs. She smiled back. The lights went green and Reynolds entered the town's main roundabout waiting for instructions.

'Where shall I go?'

'How the fuck should I know – follow the road into the centre.'

They drove passed the landmark crooked spire church on the mini ring road with Hughes looking at every turning hoping to see a familiar road.

He was looking for Derby Road, Tess's new address.

Somewhere on those streets, Tess was making her way to a bus stop, oblivious to the fact that her former lover had hijacked his prisoner escort and was hunting her down.

The pre-dawn phone call had freaked her out. *Was she right to abandon the man she once loved?* They'd met four months previously in Blackpool where she worked as a cleaner at a health centre. This handsome decorator smiled at her through the window. Next day there he was again. She popped her head outside – 'fancy a brew? I've just put the kettle on.' He flashed another warming smile.

They'd chatted – the weather, work, the usual stuff. They both knew where it was heading. Physically they were suited, roughly the same height, but, at 35, she was five years older. 'I can't believe someone as pretty as you is still on the market,' he'd flirted.

He'd fed her a load of bullshit that he'd just broken up with a girlfriend. Did she fancy a drink after work?

On their first date they did the rounds of pubs and clubs and went back to hers. He emerged from the shower naked, showing off his physique. A giant serpent's tail ran from his neck to his buttocks. In bed he'd schmoozed how he'd always preferred blondes and that she was the best-looking woman he'd ever been out with.

Several dates followed – cinema, meals out, walks in the park. He was generous, sweet and charming, and exuded a quiet authority that she found attractive.

It was all sweetness and light. Until one night in a pub when she had to pull him away from a bloke who'd said something out of turn.

Tess had discovered how his friendly charm could evaporate at the flick of a switch, particularly in drink. She'd learned to be careful how she behaved in the company of other men and whom she spoke to on a night out. He wanted to chin anyone who looked at her twice.

But she was hooked, making excuses for his complicated personality. She'd told her mates that when she got annoyed with him she knew exactly when to back off. It was his eyes, something about those eyes. Distant. Vacant. As if there was nothing actually inside.

One night, Billy had made a surprise visit to her home near the seafront. Tess opened the door in her pyjamas.

Inside, he'd grabbed her and gave her a long passionate kiss. It was unexpected and out of character. 'What's up?' she asked. He pulled her towards him again and enjoyed another prolonged kiss. After making love, he said he had a confession to make.

'Something's been troubling me babe. I've not been entirely straight.'

Teresa broke from their embrace and looked him in the eye. 'Don't tell me. You're bloody married.'

She jumped out of bed and put her nightie on. 'I knew this was too good to be true.'

'Technically, yes. But I'm leaving her. I'm getting a divorce.'

He launched a machine-gun volley of excuses. He said his missus was just an old scrubber. The only reason he'd married her was that she was the only person who wrote to him when he was inside.

'Inside where?' He'd been in prison, but 'now I've got you, that's all over,' he'd promised. Billy had tried to hug her but she'd shaken him off. 'I think you'd better go.'

Sleeping on it, she reasoned she'd overreacted. Everyone had baggage! She knocked on the door of his digs.

Then one day her brother, Tony phoned. He was renovating a house over in Derbyshire and needed a labourer. Was Billy interested?

'You fucking bet,' Billy had told Tess, 'Where does he live?'

'Chesterfield,' she said. 'Where the fuck's that?'

Two days later, Tony picked them up in his van and they were on their way to Derbyshire. They lived for a while with Tony and his wife Pat near Queen's Park.

They would start a new life together, find proper jobs, and maybe buy somewhere in the country, with a couple of pet dogs, even children perhaps. But Billy had ruined all that. How foolish she'd been. A leopard can never change its spots.

A bus came along heading for town, its lights illuminating the leaden streets. She joined the other queuing passengers, got on the bus and took her seat. Staring at the gloom outside, she thought about him again. Yes, she thought. She'd done the right thing.

'Where's Derby Road? You know Chesterfield?' Hughes screeched.

'First time here,' said Reynolds.

'You must have a map! You're a fucking taxi driver.' Hughes rummaged through the glove compartment, throwing all the contents to the floor.

With no map it was all guesswork. And they could hardly stop to ask. 'Where the fuck are we? Try next right... no left...'

They were going around in circles, all the while the floor of the taxi getting bloodier. Reynolds' TV Licence form was stained with blood. Panic set in – particularly when they hit the same roundabout again from a different direction.

Reynolds was desperate for the nightmare to end. 'Why don't you just take the car. Leave us all here. You can go where you want then. These guys could peg it. They need a hospital.'

The screws hadn't spoken for five minutes, slumped together mopping each other's wounds with the windscreen cloth.

'JUST KEEP DRIVING!' screamed Hughes.

He moved to the back of the car and leaned over the men.

'You guys are gonna have to sub me,' he said.

Simmonds handed over his wallet and whispered in the ear of his colleague. 'Don, he wants your wallet. Okay if I take it?'

Sprintall could only mumble. Simmonds rifled through his colleague's blood-stained uniform but he couldn't find it. Sprintall murmured... 'briefcase..'

Hughes frantically searched Sprintall's case. The wallet was in the lid. He turned to the driver. 'Now you son.'

Reynolds produced a five-pound note from his jacket. 'Hold on, there's more in here.' He handed over a wad of pound notes from his shirt top pocket. 'That's everything I've got on me,' he said.

As the taxi circled the town, Hughes emptied the cash onto his lap and began counting. And taunting the occupants. 'Thirty-three quid! That's fuck all! You don't get paid much, you boys.'

For ten minutes the torment continued – driving aimlessly, the two officers, still bleeding and dazed, becoming progressively weaker.

Hughes dramatically announced a decision. He ordered Reynolds to take the road out of town towards Matlock, the A632. He'd clearly given up finding Tess. He was now heading west.

After several miles he randomly insisted they turn onto the B5057 country road towards Darley Dale, a rural parish, to the south west of Chesterfield. The higher they climbed, the worse the weather became. There was now a thick covering of snow, slowing their progress.

Hughes suddenly shouted. 'STOP THE FUCKING CAR.' Reynolds pulled up on a layby next to a field. There was no-one around. And the road was deserted of vehicles. Hughes addressed Reynolds. 'See that gate? I want to see your arse disappear over it, you hear?' 'What about them?' said Reynolds.

'OUT!!!'

Reynolds struggled through the snow to the gate. He looked back. Hughes beckoned him to climb over it. Reynolds wasn't going to disobey. Hughes got out of the car and opened the rear door. He pulled the screws out like they were sacks of coal and dragged them to the verge. 'OVER THE GATE,' he screeched. It was an impossible demand.

Simmonds bent over his colleague. 'Come on Don. One big effort, yeah!' Hughes didn't wait to see if they made it. He sped off, the rear wheels spinning on the snow.

The hostages were free but in the middle of nowhere and bleeding on the roadside. If help didn't arrive soon they would perish. On this high, exposed layby, Reynolds, felt the lives of two men slipping through his fingers. Both had lost a lot of blood. Their hearts were pounding. They were weak, pale, and cold. He tried to give them first aid, but all he had was the windscreen rag.

They were bleeding badly. The one who'd been in the back was bleeding from the neck and was groggy, the other guy seemed not as bad, but was covered in blood. A car came along. Reynolds ran in the road, trying to flag it down, but it didn't stop.

After five minutes or so, all three were in the road, the prison officers staggering, and Reynolds waving frantically. Help arrived at last. It was the landlord of a nearby pub, the Red Lion, in his sports car.

'Please, please. These guys have been stabbed. Ring for an ambulance and call the police,' pleaded Reynolds. The publican sped off to dial 999.

A minute later a Landrover stopped. George McClymont, a telephone engineer, employed by the General Post Office in Chesterfield, was driving to Ashover with his colleague Mark Fisher.

He would reveal, 'I stopped and reversed. I got out and saw they were bleeding bad. They were shocked and badly shaken and handcuffed together. They asked us to take them to the nearest hospital and if we had anything to get the cuffs off with.

'I had some bolt croppers in the back and we cut through the chain. I then waved down another car that was travelling towards Chesterfield.'

The driver was Edward Miles, a Derbyshire County Council Careers Officer, in a Hillman Hunter. He would tell police, 'There was a group of men at the roadside. I thought they were workmen at first, but they said 'there's been a stabbing'.

'They asked if I could take the injured men to hospital. I said yes, but that I didn't know where the hospital was. Then one of the GPO guys said he knew the way. He got in and we put the two prison officers in the back.'

'On the way to the hospital I was told what had happened. My only comment was 'where did he get the knife from?' then one of the officers replied 'I don't know, he was searched.'

Derbyshire Police Log, Wednesday January 12th 1977.

09.56 message… 'There is a prison officer standing in the road at the second hill into Stonedge. He is asking for an Ambulance. He has another man with him.'

From: Mr Jilavu, Red Lion, Stonedge.

Received by Constable 739 Legge (Comms Room, Chesterfield West.)

Means: Telephone.

Action taken: Force Ops Room informed. Tango 156 despatched. Inspector Wigmore informed.

The first emergency call was made at 9.56am direct to Chesterfield Police station, from Mr Jilavu, the landlord of the Red Lion. It was taken by Constable Legge. The message was garbled and incomplete.

'There is a prison officer standing on the road at the second hill into Stonedge. He is asking for an ambulance. He has another man with him.'

The constable informed the force's Operations Room who sent a beat car to investigate. More vehicles stopped. One was Severn Trent Water Authority van which had radio contact with headquarters. At exactly 10am Reynolds was able to inform police – via the Water Authority- the make and registration of his taxi, and that the escaped prisoner was armed with a knife.

Derbyshire Police Log, Wednesday January 12th 1977.

10.00 message… 'A prisoner has stolen a Morris 1100, GCC 262L, having escaped from Walton. (sic) He is in possession of a Persian Blue Morris 1100 and has driven off in the direction of Matlock. This information has come from one of our vans which has been waved down by prison officers.

From: Severn Trent Water Authority

Received by: Comms Aide Williams, Comms Room, Chesterfield West.

Means: Telephone.

Action taken: Force Ops Room informed; Supt Hoggett informed; Broadcast on personal radio scheme to all officers, Chesterfield West; Unit Beat car CW 570 to Matlock Road/Slate Pit Dale; Unit Beat car CW 550 to Walton Back Lane.

This upped the ante for Derbyshire Police. The call was referred to its grand HQ, Butterley Hall, a former country home near Ripley, built in the 18th century with eight enormous bay windows and gabled attics.

Derbyshire was a well-equipped force with 1600 officers employed over four operational divisions – Derby, Alfreton, Chesterfield and Buxton.

It was led by former British Army Lieutenant Colonel, Sir Walter Stansfield, a decorated war hero, who was parachuted into France during the Second World War to organise Resistance and to direct sabotage and attacks against the Germans.

The details climbed the operation chain to the plush office of Assistant Chief Constable of Operations Alfred Mitchell.

Like many of the top brass, they were both freemasons, members of the county's oldest lodge, the 200-year-old Tyrian Lodge based in Derby.

Mitchell, who was in his fifties, was a solid-built six-foot cop who had a no-nonsense reputation. He ordered the Force into overdrive – urgent messages on phones, teleprinters and personal radios.

At 10.06 the message went out to all mobile units and police radios – '...observations requested for Morris 1100 GGC 262 L travelling towards Matlock in possession of an escaped prisoner.'

Updates came thick and fast, including a correction that car was an 1800, model, not 1100.

10.07. 'All units ...we have two prison warders, one stabbed in neck, the other in hand being treated at Chesterfield Royal Hospital Casualty.'

10.10.' Road blocks requested on main Chesterfield road into Matlock.'

At 10.15, DC Macmillan at the hospital managed to glean the name of the prisoner from the injured officers and phoned control.

'...the prisoner is William Thomas Hughes who has driven off in their taxi. He has a knife with a nine-inch blade.'

By now, every beat officer in Derbyshire was aware of the hi-jack. Road checks were already in place on main routes.

The media were alerted too, with news-flashes being organised by press officers.

Derbyshire Police Log, Wednesday January 12th 1977.

10.22 message   'GCC 262L, found on Beeley Moor crashed into ditch.'

From: Beat Officer at scene

Received by: Force Ops Room

Means: V.H.F. radio

Action taken: Scenes of Crime Officer to scene; Road check set up A57 Ladybower/Bamford; Road check set up A624 Chunal/Monks Road; Road check set up A6 Newtown lights; Road check set up A6 junction with Millers Dale Road and Tideswell crossroads. Details of incident and HUGHES passed to Buxton officers on personal radio scheme.

10.22am

Roughly 45 minutes after Hughes had made off in the taxi, a beat officer in a patrol car made a vital find. As he rounded a bend on an isolated track he saw the stolen vehicle in a ditch. It had skidded off the icy road and hit a stone wall. He was on his radio in a flash.

It was blowing a blizzard. The PC drew his truncheon and advanced gingerly. There was no-one inside, but the seats and upholstery were stained with blood, obviously fresh. The place was deserted. The snow had covered any footprints. The bonnet was still warm, and he could hear the dead engine contracting.

After a cursory search in the vicinity, there was little he could do but wait for reinforcements and go back to the warmth of his Panda.

The net would now tighten on Billy Hughes. He was on foot, dressed in a summer suit, in freezing temperatures. What's more, the point where he crashed was isolated and surrounded by snow-covered moorland.

The discovery of the crashed car sparked a flurry of police activity in that isolated corner of Derbyshire. An incident room was set up in Chesterfield. The Commander, Chief Supt Kenneth Unwin, was on leave, so the operative command was split between his deputy, Supt Barrie Wells, and Supt Thomas Hoggett under Mitchell's overall strategic direction.

The crash scene was in the Buxton South sub-division under the leadership of Chief Inspector Peter Howse, a high-flyer, who'd grown up in Derbyshire and had risen through the ranks. He set up a subsidiary incident room at Bakewell.

Four officers – Detective Sergeants Miller and Rodgers, and Detective Constables Muldoon and Bond, were summoned to the scene, along with a Scenes of Crime Unit.

The update that the taxi had been found was broadcast to all officers in the Division, along with a warning that Hughes was almost certainly now on foot and armed with a knife. Studying timings, they worked out he'd driven about four miles along a maze of icy minor roads before losing control and crashing. They were probably 20 minutes behind their man.

Patrols were told to be alive to the fact that he might have since stolen another car, or hi-jacked a vehicle and its driver, or indeed, unlikely as it seemed, had pre-arranged a rendezvous with an accomplice at that crash point.

The men at the scene put themselves in the escapee's shoes. He wouldn't get far, senior officers assured each other. They made hasty and casual conclusions. Either side of that road were miles of hostile, exposed moorland, now covered in snow. Only a madman would risk trekking those moors in that weather, particularly wearing indoor summer clothing.

The narrow track they were on led down to the village of Beeley, a parish owned by the Chatsworth Estate, with a population of around 200. Historically estate workers rented cottages there. No, it was obvious that Hughes would have followed the road down to the village a mile and a half away. They radioed in their advice and their seniors agreed. An immediate road check was set up at the Beeley village pub, the Devonshire Arms.

Mitchell, in HQ, ordered Howse to head a systematic search of all homes, farms and outbuildings leading down to Beeley.

Teams of officers and cadets, dressed in high-viz jackets, wellington boots and armed with sticks, began the operation to flush him out. A police dog handler arrived with Betsy, one of the force's best tracker dogs. Everyone stepped back as she sniffed inside the stricken vehicle for Billy's scent. There was blood on the dashboard – he'd obviously cut himself in the impact.

It was almost as if she sensed the importance of her task, excitedly wagging her tail as her handler let her off the leash. 'There you go, Betsy, go girl.'

But instead of following the human hunch and heading to the village, she leapt over the wall into a field. They all rushed to the wall.

After ten yards or so she stopped and sniffed the snow for a pee. She then turned around, jumped back over the wall, and leapt straight into the dog van. It was literally a moment of light relief for the team, although acute embarrassment for her handler who concluded she must have been confused by three different traces of blood in the taxi.

However, unlike her human masters, Betsy's instincts had proved uncannily correct.

Twenty minutes earlier

The police were right in one sense. Only a madman would take on those moors. Lawmen are trained to think rationally, fugitives aren't. They act on impulse. Instinct. And whilst police considered the only logical route for Hughes to take was the road leading down to a village, he thought differently. He'd climbed the wall. And disappeared into the wilderness.

He was 1,000 feet above sea level. The sky was low and thick with cloud. It was hilly and snowing hard. The cold air cut into his face. Pockets of mist reduced visibility to 15 yards in places.

The terrain was slippery, with concealed ditches, and boggy deep ruts that could cause serious injury and eventual death from exposure.

But he ploughed on, following his nose rather than any distant landmark. He went around in circles. At one point he came across a small stream. Rather than turn back, he took his boots and socks off, and waded through the icy water. He washed his cut forehead and wiped it on his shirt.

For four miles he'd rolled through peaks and troughs. His body began losing heat at a faster rate than it could replenish it. He became confused, disoriented, his body temperature getting dangerously low. His breathing became shallow. He was low in energy and slowing up.

He began tripping and falling over into the snow. The knife he'd used on the screws fell from his pocket and quickly became consumed by snow. Conditions were desperate. Without finding somewhere soon he might collapse with exhaustion and hypothermia.

He'd seen no sign of man nor beast. Then at last he'd heard the 'whoosh' of cars negotiating a gritted road somewhere ahead. It gave him an extra burst of energy and enthusiasm. The ground flattened. He'd reached farmland. He hadn't a clue where he was, but he saw occasional car headlights flash by, maybe a hundred yards ahead.

At the roadside he kept low, ducking behind the wall each time a vehicle approached, then waiting for a break in the traffic before stumbling further along. He saw a house with movement in the yard. It was a builder in a white van. He moved on.

And then, the smell of wood burning. Through the murk he could see smoke coming from the chimney of a cottage. An elderly woman with brown hair was working in her kitchen.

He'd randomly arrived at Pottery Cottage – the home of retired shopkeepers. He reached for his knife. It wasn't there. *Bollocks!*

He noticed a garage at the back of the complex.

Shivering and trembling, he quietly undid the latch on the five-bar gate and ambled towards the garage door. It was unlocked. Inside was a Hillman Minx, a workbench, a scattering of tools, and two axes among a pile of wood splinters. He picked them up and went back across the drive to the back door of the cottage…

11.15am

Pottery Cottage

It was just a feeling. A sixth sense. Amy was at the kitchen sink. Had someone just flashed past her eyeline? She stopped polishing the brass and looked out the window.

No-one was there. She shook her head and pondered. She might be getting on a bit, she thought, but she still had her marbles. But had she looked more closely, she would have noticed fresh footprints in the snow. Not a straight line, but a weaving trail along the drive, and around to the back of the cottage. Even closer inspection might have revealed an occasional speck of blood.

Visitors were rare. There was no need to ever lock the door during the day. But no sooner had she dismissed the sighting than there was a tap on her shoulder. She turned around.

There was a man, soaked and steaming - like a racehorse at the end of a gruelling race. He was small, and muscly, and wearing a summer suit that was caked in mud and peat. Blood ran down his face. His curly hair and eyebrows were matted with snow and ice, and his nose was running.

He moved threateningly close, his hand behind his back, holding something. Amy backed off and clutched her chest in shock. 'Oh, my... you nearly gave me a heart attack.'

'Shouldn't leave your door unlocked. You never know who might walk in.' His voice was slurred and mumbled, soft, but exuding menace. She didn't really take in what he'd said but she did notice a small tattoo on his ear lobe. He thrust a frozen nicotined finger to her lips. His hand was still shaking. The word HATE was inscribed across his knuckles and there was a swastika tattoo on his thumb.

He produced a chopping axe that was now inches from her face.

'Where'd you get that? That's Arthur's.'

It was a limp response from a mind in turmoil. But before she could speak again, he spun her into an armlock and put his hand over her mouth. He jolted her head back. She could hardly breathe.

His saturated sleeve chafed her chin. She could smell his body odour, an aroma of sweat, sleet and testosterone. His suit was dank and musty, as if it had been locked away in a closet for months.

He whispered threateningly.

'Not a word… you understand?'

In the adjoining lounge, Arthur was listening to the radio in an easy chair. 'Did you say something?' he yelled.

She couldn't speak. Indeed, it was some miracle she hadn't already fainted. 'Who's that?' the man murmured, now close enough for her to feel his spit in her eardrum. Amy managed a spluttered reply. 'My husband.'

'Call him in,' he said, tightening the grip on her throat. 'Do as I say, and you won't get hurt.' 'ARTHUR… you got a minute?'

They could hear Arthur hobbling through on his false leg. The man let go of Amy, and waited in the recess, hidden from view. Arthur slid the glass door open and came in. 'What is it?'

Like a wild cat, the man pounced, grabbing the 73-year-old around the neck from behind. They crumpled in a heap. The axe went spinning across the vinyl.

Amy stared at it for what seemed an eternity. She could easily pick it up. What should she do? Then, seeing a second axe in his belt dispelled any notion of intervention, even if she had been able to somehow muster the courage.

Arthur cut a burly figure and despite his years, was strong. He fought back, swinging his arm and catching his opponent in the face. But the attacker was much younger, around 30, fitter, stronger.

He overpowered Arthur and got on top, like a wrestler pinning down an opponent. He reached for the axe in his belt and held it menacingly above the old man's head. Amy grabbed the attacker's arm. 'Stop, stop. Don't hurt him.'

The man's voice accelerated into a frenzy. He screeched at Arthur. 'ARE YOU GONNA FUCKING CO-OPERATE?'

Every ounce of Arthur wanted to fight back. He was a brave, proud, man. But he was also a realist. What chance would a one-legged pensioner have? He nodded acceptance. The man got up and stood over him, this time wielding the axe as insurance rather than as a threat.

'On your feet.' Amy helped her husband onto a kitchen chair. He was shocked and dazed … but still defiant. 'Whatever it is you're playing at son, you won't get away with it…'

'ARTHUR! PLEASE!' Amy pleaded.

She turned to the intruder. 'Please listen to me. Look at us… we're hardly a threat. You don't need all this violence.'

The man retrieved the stray axe and wedged it in his belt. They watched as he rummaged through the cutlery draw and found a boning knife. He slipped it into his pocket. He sat on a kitchen chair and began to prise his boots off. His sodden socks were virtually fused to his feet.

'Here. Let me.' She pulled them off and took them through to put them in front of the lounge fire.

She returned and looked at Arthur. 'Arthur. Give him the car keys.' And then to the man. 'The car's in the garage. Take it!' But he wasn't going anywhere – at least, not yet.

'I need to lie low for a couple of hours, dry out, and I'll be out of your way.' The menace had gone from his voice. Amy felt a hint of relief. The man paced the floor, deep in thought and still shivering.

'You're freezing. You need to get out of those clothes or you'll get pneumonia. I'll find you some warm things then you can get off when you're ready.'

Arthur glared at him from the table, determined not to show any sign of weakness, not even a blink. 'What is it you want?' she asked.

He ignored her. 'Is there anyone else in?'

'No,' she said. 'My daughter and her husband are at work and our granddaughter's at school.'

'What about neighbours?'

'They're away. I've got their door key if you want. I do their cleaning. You can hide there! No one will know and we won't tell, will we Arthur?' Arthur spoke. 'I've seen off bigger than you, son.'

'For goodness sake, Arthur, just do as he says!'

The man went to the kettle. Amy thought he was about to make a cup of tea. Instead, he chopped off the electric flex with the axe.

'I'm gonna tie you up 'til I get my mind straight,' he said to Arthur. The old man winced as the flex cut into his skin.

43

'Show some compassion. He's 73,' Amy pleaded. She was wasting her breath. He pulled it even tighter.

Arthur could only retaliate verbally. 'Bet you've never done a day's work in your life, have you son?'

The man squared up to Arthur's face. 'You remind me of my old man, you know that?'

He moved towards the window and looked out. 'What time your daughter home?' 'Usually about half three,' said Amy.

Amy went to the cupboard for a saucepan. 'I'll make us a nice hot drink.' The man relaxed. 'If you can persuade your man here not to be stupid, I won't harm you. Is that a deal?'

Amy nodded in compliance. Arthur scowled. 'Who are you?,' he said. 'My name's Billy…'

He looked out the window again, on constant alert.

'I'm on the run from the police.'

The couple swopped anxious glances.

Derbyshire Police Log, Wednesday January 12ᵗʰ 1977.

11.31am message: Report on condition of prison officers at Chesterfield Royal Hospital – officer Sprintall has severe lacerations to neck and is having operation to arrest bleeding.'

From: Supt Barratt at the hospital.

Received by: Supt. Hoggett

Means: Telephone.

Action taken: Scenes of Crime Officer to hospital for photograph.

11.32 message: Blackpool Police informed of incident and requested to check the home addresses of Hughes' wife and mother.

13

With his brutal entrance, Hughes had taken physical and psychological control of his hostages. He was sure they wouldn't give him any trouble - at least not in the short term.

Amy tried appeasement, to make him a friend not a foe. Her instinct was to jolly him along, then hopefully he would soon leave them in peace. She'd even made them all a cup of tea, giving the man a plate of biscuits and hand-washed his wet socks and put them in the tumble dryer.

It was typical of her character – kind, thoughtful, a willingness to make the best of whatever bad situation life threw at her.

He talked calmly, with none of the previous hostility and menace. 'Right, we're going on a tour,' he said, untying Arthur.

They went through the ground floor room by room, Amy leading the way. She could have been an estate agent, showing a prospective buyer around. She explained that of the four properties, one was empty and a couple of teachers, The Newmans, lived at the end.

'We moved here seven years ago. It's a lovely spot. Gill and Sarah, our granddaughter, walk the dogs across the moors.'

The Moran's kitchen - country-style with an Aga cooker, round table and chairs, and dresser with rows of posh plates on display, was spotless. He pushed them into the lounge - 18ft long and 14 feet wide. It had the feel of a country inn, cosy and warm, with a wooden beam decorated with brass fittings, and an inglenook fireplace dressed with a brass coal scuttle, fireplace tools and a cooking cauldron hooked under the mantlepiece.

It was comfortable, not flashy or pretentious, with four easy chairs and a dark wood coffee table nestling on a plush fitted patterned carpet. A bookshelf contained works on the US President John F. Kennedy, and a new 24-inch colour TV graced the corner.

'What's through there?' he asked, pointing at the brick archway at the end. 'The dining room. They like to entertain,' said Amy.

They walked through. A dining table with six chairs dominated the room parked on a parquet floor. Through the French windows they could see the sleet falling outside. There was a radiogram with a rack of

LPs, with the face of French heartthrob Sacha Distel smiling back at them. A hostess trolley was parked beside a glass and gold drinks trolley, stocked with spirits and sherry. Hughes lifted a decanter, smelt the contents, and took a swig. It was whisky. 'That's my first drink in months,' he joked. Amy responded with a polite smile. Arthur wasn't amused.

Upstairs, he popped his head inside the bathroom and checked out the Morans' bedroom. Their double bed was partly covered by a velvety maroon throw. It was a big room – the same dimensions as the lounge below – with fitted wardrobes, a dressing table and stool.

On the bedside table was a Teasmade – a combined alarm clock, radio and teamaker. He examined it – then swiftly chopped the flex off the machine with his axe, splintering the wood of the table. That single act of wanton vandalism appalled Amy almost as much as anything that had gone before. 'What do you think you're doing?' she said. 'That table cost a lot of money.'

Hughes merely smirked. There was a row of family pictures. He picked up a framed photograph of Gill and Richard in front of a church. It was their wedding picture. He couldn't take his eyes off Gill. 'Lucky boy, eh.'

'She looked so beautiful. We're so proud of her,' said Amy. Arthur spoke. 'You lay one finger on her and I'll…'

'…What, hit me with your false leg!'

There was a photo of Gill, Richard and Sarah on a family holiday in Spain, and a celebration snap of Richard with a garland around his neck at some motoring event. 'A bit of a boy racer, is he?'

'It's his hobby,' said Amy.

'How's he afford that?'

'He's a very successful businessman, a very fine man. We're lucky to have him as our son-in-law. He's a wonderful father and does a lot for charity,' she added.

Arthur piped in – 'Amazing what you can achieve by a bit of hard work.'

Hughes said nothing, just pushed them both into the landing where she showed him Sarah's room and the spare bedroom, sparse and functional, with two single beds and two chairs. The tour was over.

14

11.35am

Chesterfield town centre

Despite the weather, Gill Moran had had a good journey in, and had managed to get a space in the multi-storey. Perhaps people were taking the day off, she thought.

She worked as a shorthand typist at John Roberts accountants in Chesterfield. The hours were ideal for a working mother – 9am until 3pm. This enabled her to ferry Sarah to and from school if needs be, although these days her daughter preferred to come home on the school bus.

Her days were spent taking dictation from her boss and writing letters to the taxman and clients. In their business accuracy was crucial, especially over figures, and she was a reliable and accurate typist, always double-checking amounts before putting the letters back in the tray for signing.

That morning she arrived punctually, discussed the forecast with colleagues, made a cup of coffee, chatted, and took the cover off her electric typewriter.

On her desk was a picture of the three of them enjoying ice cream at Scarborough the previous summer. There was also a holiday brochure which she liked to browse in her breaks. She slipped her boots off and put her flat slippers on ready to tackle her in-tray.

Mid-morning she always phoned home. She lifted receiver to dial out…..
***

The petrol blue phone ringing in the hall sent Hughes into a panic. 'Answer it. FUCKING ANSWER IT!'

As Amy reached for the receiver, Billy held his knife to Arthur's throat. 'One false word…'

Amy's voice faltered. 'Hello.'

'Hi Mum. What's the weather doing?'

Amy looked across at Arthur. He was in a state of shock, visibly shaking under the strain of imprisonment and the frustration of being unable to do anything about it. She tried to answer Gill's question, but the words just wouldn't come out. She was just too choked to speak.

'Mum… you there?'

Amy swallowed hard. 'Sorry love.'

'Are you okay?' said Gill.

Amy looked at Arthur again. Billy moved the knife nearer to her husband's throat.

'They reckon we might get more snow tonight. Be careful. You hear?' said Amy.

Gill was relieved. There'd been no crisis at home.

'I'll use it as an excuse to sneak off early,' she said.

Amy immediately became more agitated.

'What time? You can't just walk out. I need to know what time you're coming home.'

Gill glanced at the receiver puzzled. Her mother was usually so carefree and friendly. Yet there was a sense of apprehension in the tone of her voice. She changed the subject.

'I was thinking of getting some chops. How we doing for veg?'

'You think that all I've got to do all day is check the bloody veg!'

Gill was now worried about her mother's mental state. This aggression was so out of character.

'You sure everything's all right?'

Amy murmured a 'yes' into the mouthpiece.

'I'll get some anyway… must go.'

'Wait…

'Gill!' said Amy.

'Yes, mum.'

'I love you..'

'Yes… me too,' said Gill.

She put the phone down and stared at it for a few seconds. What an earth was that all about? She needed to finish the dictation if she wanted to leave early so she resumed typing.

In Pottery Cottage, Billy ripped the phone out of the wall.

15

Detective Inspector Hulme at Chesterfield rang the Lancashire force to warn that Hughes had escaped. They advised that a round-the-clock watch be set up at the homes of his wife in Blackpool and his mother in Preston.

Time was certainly on their side. The distance between Chesterfield and the west coast was approaching 100 miles. Even if Hughes had somehow seized possession of another car, it would be around three hours or so before he reached the seaside town.

The DI's call was answered by PC Marsden. He eventually spoke to a 31-year-old detective constable called Bob Ashworth.

There wasn't much Blackpool Police didn't know about William Thomas Hughes. He was regarded there as a schizophrenic, likely one day to kill somebody.

Ashworth had once arrested Hughes and his younger brother Alan for breaking into a chemist. He'd bitten through Ashworth's jacket wounding his arm. During the same fight, one of the officer's mates, Phil Goodison, a 14-stone detective, was almost strangled as the Hughes boys fought back.

The brothers were overpowered and put in a police van. But on the way to the nick they ripped a seat off the van interior and used it as a battering ram to break open the back door. They fled onto a housing estate, but were eventually cornered.

In the police station they'd become extremely violent. Officers received kicks, blows and bites to their bodies. In all, six officers were assaulted, several needing hospital treatment. And later in the police cells Billy butted another officer in the face, breaking his nose.

After they'd appeared in court that day, Billy had gone berserk and ripped out the complete central heating system in the cells at the Central Police Office in Blackpool.

But he could be meek and mild too. After a break-in at a house he found Billy hiding in a garden shed.

'He was sitting on the floor like a kid. But that's him all over – one minute total violence, the next calm as anything.

'He has this sort of blank look in his eyes. He could be talking to you, but you weren't there. It was like a shield had come down. I've only seen that look once before - on the face of a man who shot dead one of our officers,' said Ashworth.

Shortly after noon, officers from Lancashire Police arrived at a shabby flat above a fruit shop in Blackpool where Jean Hughes lived with a friend Alice, a former partner of Billy's brother Alan, who was away in prison. They rammed on the door with a firmness that implied their mission was urgent. But there was no immediate reply.

The male PC yelled through the letter box. 'Mrs Hughes… Lancashire Police. We know you're in there.'

They could hear mild panic inside. After a while the door opened a few inches. The chain was still on. They saw the face of a tiny, frail woman, probably seven stone. Her lipstick was smeared and she looked bedraggled, much older than her 26 years.

'When you lot gonna learn,?' she said. 'There's nothing here, and both our men are away. You should know that anyhow.'

The female officer spoke first. 'It's about Billy, Mrs Hughes.'

The colour drained from Jean Hughes' cheeks. 'What about him?' she said.

'Can we come in?' said the WPC.

Jean released the security chain and the officers walked inside. In the front room they found Alice, dressed in a shellsuit and smoking on the settee. Three toddlers played on the floor amid toys.

The officers took stock - peeling wallpaper, threadbare furnishings, a little black and white telly, ashtrays full of fag ends – and the whiff of soiled nappies. The male PC spoke first, addressing the woman on the sofa. 'And you are?'

Jean replied on her behalf. 'She's Alice. It's okay.'

There was no point in dressing up what they had to say.

'Billy's done a runner. Escaped from custody on the way to court.'

Jean leapt into a frenzy, picking up Billy's child Nicola off the floor, and grabbing some clothes from the ironing pile. 'We're not staying here,' she said.

The WPC intervened. 'We know in the past he's made some threats against you and your other daughter, Mrs Hughes.'

'Threats!' Jean pulled down the zip of her shell suit to reveal a scar down her neck.

'You got any idea where he might be heading, Mrs Hughes?' said the female constable. 'Fuck knows,' she replied.

'Look, you're perfectly safe for a while at least. It only happened a couple of hours ago. The words calmed her down.

What can you tell us about him?' asked the WPC.

Jean lit a cigarette and told the officers everything they wanted to know. She said they'd met five years previously. She was living in a boarding house in Blackpool with her seven-year-old daughter, Tracey. A friend asked if she could find room for this bloke who'd just come out of the nick for burglary.

'I weren't too bothered about his record. I was no angel myself, she said. 'I couldn't believe me luck, to be honest. He was a looker, gentle, polite, nothing like what he turned out to be.'

She fell for him immediately. That night they went out for a drink and shared the same bed. They'd flitted from flat to flat around Blackpool, duping landlords of their rent. He had no job but survived by screwing houses. After six weeks she discovered she was pregnant and was thrilled to be carrying his child.

When she went into labour he was there beside her, but at the crucial moment felt sick and nearly blacked out. He rushed out of the delivery room and didn't see Nicola born.

Jean puffed on her cigarette. 'A big tough guy like that, but he couldn't stand the sight of blood!'

She said at first, he'd fussed over his daughter but soon resented the attention Jean was giving her. Three days after she left hospital Billy hit her as she was feeding the child. He said he wanted his breakfast and that he should come first. One day she'd cooked him four different meals. Each time he threw the food back in her face.

There were further bouts of extreme violence. Friends begged her to leave him. But she couldn't. Just couldn't. He had this hold over her. Not just physical fear but emotional dependency too.

'I knew what he was, but I still loved him,' said Jean.

It was a tale the officers had heard many times. Battered wife syndrome, they called it at the nick.

Three days before Nicky's first birthday he was sentenced with his brother Alan for burglary at a pharmacy and wounding two coppers.

He'd written regularly from Walton jail, then on one visit proposed to her across the table. They married in the prison chapel with Jean forking out for the special licence and the rings. They were given an hour together - in his cell.

She'd styled her hair into shoulder-length curly blonde locks, saved up for a catalogue dress, and took him a fresh carnation to wear in the lapel of his favourite navy suit.

Jean got up to fetch a picture to show the officers but the woman looked at her watch.

'We'll arrange for a safe house but we want to stress it's just a precaution,' said the male.

Jean stubbed out the cigarette and started to pack her bags.

16

2.55pm

Chesterfield town centre

In a supermarket on the outskirts of Chesterfield, Gill Moran bought a packet of chops, some vegetables for dinner, and a packet of twenty Gold Leaf. She'd managed to get off early because of the weather. Forecasters were predicting heavy snow later that evening.

Had she been a minute earlier in that store she might have heard an urgent newsflash on Radio Hallam, the local station.

"News just in… a prisoner has escaped on the way to court in Chesterfield after stabbing two police officers. He took off in a taxi which has been found abandoned on the outskirts of the town. Derbyshire Police are warning all households to lock their doors. More on that in our later bulletins."

Inside Pottery Cottage, Billy was pacing up and down at the kitchen window waiting for her to arrive.

'She's late,' he said.

His agitation was a warning signal for Amy.

'It's fine. She's probably taking it easy on the road.'

Gill was indeed finding the driving tough. There seemed to be a lot of police activity which she put down to the conditions. Some cars were being stopped, others stuck in the snow. Only two hundred yards from the cottage she saw three police cars outside the local pub. She wondered if anything had happened. At 3.05 Gill pulled into the drive.

Gill's main emotion was relief to be home, followed by irritation that the gate on the drive was open, swinging in the wind.

From the lounge window, Billy watched her Hillman Avenger swing around to the back. He grabbed Arthur and put the knife to his throat. He barked out orders to Amy.

'When she arrives you answer the door, and don't say a fucking word.'

Gill put the car in the garage and walked around to the rear kitchen door. As was customary in the North of England, folks tended to use the back door. Gill tried to open it, but it was locked. Another irritation! She began fumbling for her keys, but within a heartbeat, Amy was there, at the door. There were no hellos.

'Mum, please close the gate. The dogs will be in Sheffield before we know it. And why is the door locked?'

As Gill stepped inside, she sensed tension in her Mum's face and demeanour. Amy looked at her daughter, held her arm and said briefly, 'Don't panic, Gill.'

Gill's first thought was that something had happened to Dad – or to Sarah at school.

Billy had told her what to say and she was following his script.

'We've got a man here. He's hiding from the police. He's got a knife, but he's not going to harm us. He's with Dad in the lounge… but it's going to be all right Gill.'

At that moment, the man came into the kitchen. He was back in his navy suit and holding her dad's boning knife.

He looked at Gill. 'Hello. I'm not going to hurt you.'

She followed him through to the lounge. Her father was sunk in a chair, the hopelessness of his situation etched on his face. She ran to give him a cuddle.

The man made her sit down and again repeated his soft injunction that there was nothing to be frightened of if they simply did as they were told. Then he said matter-of-factly that he'd escaped from a taxi and the police were after him. He'd attacked two prison officers – to wound, but not to kill. 'I could've killed them. I know how to kill.'

It was a sinister message delivered in a calm, measured manner. Then his tone changed to one of contempt. 'The police might be doing house to house, but they ain't very clever. I need to think of something.'

There was fear in the room, certainly, but surprisingly, Gill was quite calm. She still hadn't completely taken in the full extent of what had happened- a fugitive in her home, giving orders and waving a knife about. The only thing she could do, she thought, was make everyone a cup of coffee. 'Do you take sugar?' she asked.

'Two… and it's Billy.'

They all stood in the kitchen drinking from mugs while he sat at the table explaining what he'd done, even down to the fact that he'd taken some of the prisoner officers' money.

Gill had trouble catching what he was saying because of his Lancashire accent and quiet voice.

After coffee he got up and locked the communicating door between the two kitchens. He then went to the back door and locked that. He was accumulating a collection of internal keys on a ribbon of attached to the belt loops of his trousers.

'It's just like being a screw,' he said.

Gill looked at the clock. Sarah would be home soon. She wondered what on earth she would say to her.

17

3.30pm

Derbyshire Police Headquarters

By mid-afternoon, more than 200 officers were involved in the manhunt, visiting farms, searching out-buildings, and manning road checks. From mid-morning, information on the escape had been given to the media with warnings that he was likely to be dangerous if challenged.

There were seven local radio stations in the wider area – BBC Radio Sheffield and Radio Hallam based in Sheffield, one at Derby, two further south at Nottingham, and two over the Pennines serving Manchester and some of the High Peaks. ·

The main evening newspaper, the Sheffield Star, managed to scramble the story onto its front page, along with a picture of the wanted man, as did its sister paper, The Chesterfield Star.

Derbyshire's head of CID made a TV appeal, asking the public to report any sightings of Hughes whatsoever. 'He is undoubtedly a very violent man. He's got to be caught very quickly. The one thing we DON'T want the public to do is to have a go at this man. We still think he might be armed with a knife.'

Local radio was running the story every hour and word spread quickly across the countryside and worried residents began to take precautions.

Mr Shirt, a farmer, of Syda Farm, Holymoorside, kept a 12-bore shotgun by his side all day. He'd been alerted by phone within half an hour of the hi-jacked taxi being found. Then police arrived at his farm with tracker dogs and searched his haylofts, barns and outbuildings. When darkness fell they returned every hour. It was the same with his son at nearby Rufford House Farm.

In her smallholding at Uppertown near Ashover, where Betty Marriott farmed alone, she posted a dog in her grounds.

'There is an uneasy fear among neighbours but apart from locking our doors, there is little we can do, but I must admit that I feel frightened,' she said.

The force was fixated by the notion Hughes had taken the road and not the moors. On that basis they only searched isolated farms and other dwellings and small communities to the west of the crash site. Some properties in the radius of the abandoned car were searched twice, others not at all.

On Long Lane, a stone's throw from Pottery Cottage, there were three farms. The farmers there expressed anger that there hadn't been a policeman in sight.

It was all a bit haphazard on the roads too. At some checks, police searched the back of vans and lorries, whilst at other points they merely asked drivers to produce their driving licenses.

Mitchell at HQ was convinced Hughes had been heading towards Lancashire in the taxi. It was therefore a reasonable assumption that he would still make towards the A6, which was about two and a half miles downhill from where the taxi crashed, probably concealing himself until he could obtain further transport.

Mitchell ordered search teams to ensure that 1) the occupants were safe and 2) Hughes had not secured any hiding place before nightfall.

At Bakewell police station the man in charge of the local search, Chief Inspector Howse, assembled giant Ordnance Survey maps of the area and briefed all the team. He laid down the following criteria;

All isolated farms and property were to be visited and searched, with a dog handler allocated to each of the three areas outlined on the OS maps; all property and out-buildings to be searched, even if someone was at home; if no-one was at home, the outside perimeter of premises to be searched for signs of break-in and entry. If an occupant was inside, officers should always invite themselves into the premises to ensure all is in order.

They were reminded too that in the countryside, there was every likelihood of easy access to shotguns, and this was always a possibility as far as Hughes was concerned.

The downside of publicity was an overload of information from the public. Response was overwhelming, with reporting of sightings all over the patch. Police were flooded with calls. Every stranger on a street, every open shed door, even dogs barking, came under suspicion.

Derbyshire Police Log, Wednesday January 12ᵗʰ 1977.

11.39 message… Dogs barking at Syda House Farm Holymoorside.
From: Member of public
Action taken: Supt Barratt and officers to farm.
Result: Premises checked. In order.

12. 48 message… Request for vehicle check on car travelling towards Chesterfield carrying two males and one female.
From: Member of public
Action taken: Police National Computer Check
Result: Not connected with enquiry.

12.53 message… Man answering Hughes description walking along road at Spitewinter.
From: A passing lorry driver
Action taken: Supt Barratt and officers to Spitewinter.
Result: Search negative.

A gamekeeper on the vast Chatsworth Estate, two miles from the crash site, reported smoke coming from the woods. A dozen officers descended on the scene armed with baseball bats and sticks. They found two teenagers around a fire. They'd bunked off school.

Someone in control noticed that Derby County were entertaining Blackpool – Billy's home club – in an FA Cup tie at the Baseball Ground that evening. It created a frisson of excitement. Might Hughes attend the game and try to grab a lift back to the West Coast? It was a longshot, for sure, but a dozen officers were drafted in to mingle with the away fans.

Checks were set up at Derby Railway Station and arrangements put in place to intercept coaches full of supporters. As it turned out, the match was cancelled due to the weather and the men were reassigned to search properties.

18

3.40pm

Wigley Primary School

Sarah Moran loved her ten minutes of independence on the school bus. It made her feel grown-up, and she could chat to her friends away from the ears of prying adults.

It had been a busy term. The class project was all about their playground, the Peak District National Park. The subject matter was calculated to tap into pupils' natural curiosity about the locality whilst at the same time embracing key subjects such as local history, geography, and geology.

Sarah's class discovered how it had taken millions of years for nature to create its unique landscape. Once there'd been practically nothing – just a vast, shallow sea of microscopic shelled creatures covering the land.

They learned about volcanoes, the Ice Age, how the caves, caverns and rivers were formed; how dinosaurs had once roamed the area along with the mammoth, woolly rhinoceros and the arctic fox; and how the Romans, Saxons, Vikings, and Normans fought over its riches and built fortresses and castles.

Sarah's bus passed the Highwayman Inn, 300 yards or so from her home. It was the signal for her to collect her things as it slowed.

'Sarah. It's you..' called the driver.

He pulled up in the layby immediately outside her home.

'Take care love,' he said and watched her onto the drive before pulling away.

From behind the curtains, Billy was watching too. But instead of going straight inside the cottage, she stopped and scooped up handfuls of snow. She made snowballs and threw them at the garage door.

They could hear the thud from inside.

'I'll get her in,' said Gill, making for the door. But Billy stopped her. 'Leave her be, she's having fun.'

Next they heard her knocking on the back door. Amy went to let her in. 'Come in, darling. Quickly.'

Sarah kicked the snow off her shoes, and went into the kitchen. Gill was determined that everything should appear normal, but she couldn't help rushing towards her daughter and kissing her, asking if she'd had a good day at school.

'We've a visitor,' said Gill, leading her to the lounge.

Billy greeted the little girl with a smile. His knife was covered up by his jacket and the two axes were nowhere to be seen. Arthur and Amy were sitting down.

'This gentleman's car has broken down and he's waiting for the AA to come and mend it,' said Gill.

'Hello,' said Billy. 'What's your name?'

Gill replied on her behalf. 'This is Sarah.'

'Where is it? I didn't see it on the drive,' Sarah replied.

Billy interjected – 'Just up the road. Your mum's a very kind lady letting me use the phone and letting me wait here,' he said.

'He might be here for a while,' said Gill. 'They need to bring a replacement car.'

Sarah shrugged and asked to make a snowman.

'It's too cold. Besides, it'll be dark soon. Why don't you do some sewing?' Gill said.

'Oh, I'm good at that,' said Billy.

'Men don't sew,' said Sarah.

'Ah, that's where you're wrong,' said Billy, quietly. 'I've done a lot of it in my time.' He looked across at the adults but none of them thought it funny.

Amy went to go upstairs to get Sarah's sewing box. But a few steps up she saw Billy's axes. She grabbed some ironing to hide them from view and took the bundle to the kitchen.

Gill made more coffee and brought in a tray. All the adults drank it and smoked cigarettes – Billy refusing her Gold Leaf brand, saying he preferred John Player Special.

Sarah was on the floor making a patchwork cushion. At one stage Billy got up and went over to her. He'd noticed she couldn't re-thread her sewing needle and said, 'here, let me do that. I'm good at needles.'

He held it to the light and slid the thread through the eye first time without even squinting. The little girl smiled and said thank you. His charm offensive was working on her at least.

Gill began to relax, even thinking for a moment that this man really <u>was</u> a stranded motorist waiting for help. They were all hanging on to his insistence that come nightfall he would be off and out of their hair.

But that brief calm evaporated in an instant. Sarah went to the kitchen for a drink and moved the laundry. She screamed as the axes fell to the floor. 'What are these?' she shouted. Gill rushed through. Sarah was examining them – 'put them down. Grandad's been using them. He'll be cross.'

Billy came in, but Gill had already put them back under the ironing. Sarah went to her room to play.

Gill noticed that the phone was out of the wall, the wiring exposed for all to see. What if Sarah spotted it? The cover story that the stranger had used the phone would be blown. She quietly mentioned it to Billy, adding that it would be suspicious if people were trying to ring and might report it.

Billy smiled – 'You're quite smart,' he said, then threw the phone at Arthur. 'Don't just sit there, mend the bloody thing.'

Billy summoned Gill upstairs. He made her partly fill the bath and said that if the police came Amy would answer the door and say that Gill was having a bath. If this happened, he would stay in the bathroom with her, along with Sarah and Arthur.

Meanwhile Arthur was in the hall, reconnecting the phone. He wasn't buying this intruder's promise that he would leave. Billy was upstairs out of the way. Could he quietly ring 999? Or make a bolt out the door? Every escape thought went through his mind.

But he figured that with the neighbours not back until Friday, even if he could hobble down to the nearby pub, Billy could do untold harm to his family. It was foolhardy to even consider it.

Billy came down and patrolled the lounge and kitchen, slightly edgier than even a few minutes before. He was up and down the stairs all the time. It gave Sarah quite a fright when this stranger suddenly put his head around her bedroom door and then disappeared in a flash.

Billy went to the kitchen and unlocked the connecting doors to let the dogs in. They were the only ones that day who were pleased to see him. He was very friendly with them, stroking their chins, patting them. They seemed to like him.

Sarah came down and said she wanted to watch TV. She switched it on, but when she put the lamp on, the bulb popped and the TV went off. Billy said he'd mend it and asked Gill if she had any 13-amp fuses which she found in a drawer. Billy took the plug to pieces but couldn't get the TV to work. Arthur joined him, fiddling with the fuses.

Sarah gave up on TV and went to the kitchen with Amy to do some more sewing.

The silence of the cottage was broken by the shrill of the telephone ringing in the hall. It threw everyone. For a split second, they all froze. The phone had been out of service until only a minute ago and neither Billy, nor anyone else, had thought about what to do if it actually rang!

He sprang into action. On the third or fourth peal, he summoned Gill to answer it. There were no instructions what she should say, except for her to talk normally. He listened with his ear next to the receiver, his arm around her waist. He could smell her perfume.

Amy distracted Sarah in the kitchen with idle chat. Arthur listened from the lounge. It was Gill's friend, Ann Goldthorpe, the wife of Richard's co-director, who lived in a neighbouring village.

'Hi Gill, it's Ann.'

Gill responded with a weak hello.

'Have you heard the news?

'No.'

'There's an escaped prisoner on the loose. All very dramatic!,' said Ann. Billy tightened his grip.

'He's very dangerous, apparently. It's been on the radio all day.' She was so scared she'd asked her husband Paul to come home early. 'Is Richard home yet,?'

Gill replied as matter-of-factly as she could. No, Richard wasn't home yet, and they would take care and would lock the doors. Gill thanked her for the tip and politely rang off.

Billy, now uncomfortably close, looked her in the eye, and whispered 'well done.'

The call seemed to send Billy's stress levels up a gear. He couldn't sit still, going up and down the stairs, and in and out of the kitchen where the others were all assembled.

62

In an instant he was back in the lounge, outing all the lights and opening the curtains so he could see out.

He began chopping the electric wires from appliances and storing the leads in his belt and pocket. At times, Arthur's boning knife fell out of his pocket and onto the floor.

Sarah sensed a rise in tension. 'Mummy, I don't like that man. Why has he got a knife and going all over the house collecting wires?'

Gill answered as calmly as she could, explaining that it was obviously something to do with his car. He was worried about the AA and was looking out for them.

She put the oven grill on and started peeling potatoes. They all ate chops, chips and peas. Billy remained quiet throughout, the others talking about routine things because of Sarah.

Billy then started asking about Richard. What time would he be in? What sort of a man was he? Would he cause him trouble?

Amy told him that he was as gentle as a lamb and would do as he was told. Gill nodded in agreement. Arthur wondered if that was the right thing to say.

Billy said he was deciding exactly when to leave and asked Gill if she had any maps. 'No, but Richard has got some in his car.'

Arthur, who had been silent for a while, said he had a map in his vehicle in the garage. Billy then took Gill to the garage to look in Dad's car. Arthur again wondered about raising the alarm. But this guy seemed adamant that he was leaving.

In the garage all they could find was an old AA book and they went back inside with it.

As Gill and Amy washed up, Sarah asked if she could watch telly in grandad's house. Arthur looked at Billy who got up and went through to the Minton's quarters. Out of sight he cut the phone wire and beckoned them through.

He then retired to the lounge, sitting in the dark, waiting for Richard's car to pull into the drive.

19

5.30pm

M1 Motorway, Derbyshire

Richard Moran headed home after a successful business meeting in Birmingham. He'd wined and dined clients and managed to squeeze a good price. He'd always had a good sales patter - empathetic, and likeable - with a gentle sense of humour.

At 41, it was fair to say that life was pretty perfect. He had a top job - partner and sales director in his own business – a good income, his own home, and a loving, supportive family.

The Morans shared the same philosophy about life. It was to be enjoyed, not endured. And they lived it to the full, without ever going over the top. They liked to entertain and be entertained. The previous weekend for example they'd danced until the early hours at a dinner party with friends enjoying topside and gooseberry fool and a bottle or two of Lambrusco.

But they gave something back to the community too. They supported the local church, school events and charities, and were generous donators of time and money. Richard had just been elected to the Rotary Club and donated several years of service to the junior Chesterfield Round Table where Gill also served on the Ladies Committee.

They'd met in the summer of 1958, shortly after Gill's 20th birthday. She worked as a typist and driver for a car components company in Birmingham. One day she was delivering parts to a building firm and they were signed for by a good-looking young man with an Irish accent.

He was three years her senior and there was an attraction both ways. But the shy Richard didn't have the guts to ask her out. Instead, he asked another girl to approach her on his behalf. It worked, and he took her to a dance in Birmingham's Trentham Gardens.

She found him charming and amusing and sensed that he was serious about her. And boy, could he lay on the blarney. She was very pretty, he said, and would be married very soon. A girl like her wouldn't be on the shelf for long. Then he added, 'If you're not married within a year I will marry you myself.'

That autumn they became engaged and a year later married. He had no money, he said, but had energy and ambition. He would do his best for her. And he proved true to his word.

He now earned the salary to provide the material comforts of executive living – a company car, holidays abroad - and he had the character to give her the warmth and affection of a sound marriage. They both dressed well and he could even afford to start a wine cellar and indulge in his hobby of motor sport.

The only hiccough in their 17 years together was that they couldn't have children of their own. They'd tried for several years, but doctors had told them it was never going to be. They decided to adopt, and applied to the local authority. Assessors considered them perfect potential parents – stable, financially secure, god-fearing and decent. In December 1968 they became the proud parents of a beautiful baby girl they named Sarah.

When Richard was climbing the career ladder his work took him to Derbyshire. They had a place in Tupton, then he found Pottery Cottage, ideal for conversion into a double home, and Gill was thrilled when her parents chipped in and moved up too. They'd been there for seven years.

Richard had a choice of route back to their home. He could have left the M1 early, but rather than go the fiddly route and avoid traffic, he stayed on the motorway until Junction 29.

He swung his sporty red Chrysler 180 to the inside lane and turned off. He was ten miles from home – straight into Chesterfield and out west on the other side to Eastmoor. He figured the main roads would be gritted and he was correct.

He couldn't possibly have known that earlier that day a prisoner in a taxi had attacked two prison warders at that very spot. Besides, Hughes' escape didn't merit a place in national news bulletins. They were more concerned with the unveiling of the world's first personal computer in Chicago; an eruption of that Mount Nyiragongo in Zaire, and that Jimmy Carter was about to be sworn in as President of the United States.

He'd spent the journey home mulling over his meeting and singing along to the music on Radio 2. He felt guilty that he hadn't had time to ring Gill about dinner. He'd had a large lunch and only wanted a snack. However, he would be in time to read to Sarah.

***

Billy sat in the lounge, his eyes glued to the darkness outside. He'd turned the lights out and created a gap in the curtains so he could see the headlights flash by when Richard eventually pulled into the drive.

They'd all assured him that Richard wouldn't be any trouble. But Billy wasn't so sure. He figured that any man worth his salt would put up a fight, especially to protect his family. He was ready for a battle of supremacy. Two alpha males.

He'd instructed his hostages what to do when Richard walked through that door. And, buoyed by his repeated assurances that he'd be off by nightfall, they were ready to obey his every command.

Amy saw him first. From the kitchen. 'Richard's home, Gill.'

The adults moved to their places like actors in a play. Gill rushed to the lounge to join Billy, whilst Amy waited at the back door to greet her son-in-law. Arthur and Sarah were still next-door watching TV.

Billy stood behind Gill with his left arm around her neck. With his other hand he held her Dad's knife to her throat.

Richard barely had time to try the door handle before Amy was there, urging him to come inside. She touched his arm and spoke to him, attempting whispered reassurance. But nothing could have prepared him for he was about to see.

By the time he reached the lounge he was ashen-faced and looking dazed. He looked across the room. There was his wife, frozen with fear, with a stranger holding a knife to her throat.

'Don't come near or I'll kill her,' said the man.

'Whoaa.. take it easy,' said Richard. 'What the hell's going on?'

He looked plaintively at Gill. He so wanted to run and cuddle her, but daren't.

'You know this man?' he asked. Gill could only nod. Was that a no, or a yes?

'He's been here all day,' said Amy. He'd escaped from the police and would be leaving anytime soon.

Richard took stock of the room. 'Where's Sarah?'

'Next door with Dad,' muttered Gill.

Richard held out his car keys. 'I've half a tank. The roads are empty. We won't phone anyone.'

Gill blurted out. 'I told him you'd co-operate. See, Billy, I said, didn't I?'

Richard was puzzled by the familiarity. But Billy continued to hold the knife at Gill's throat. She could feel the sharp tip against her skin. He barked a command at her husband.

'Down on the floor. Now!!! If you're as good as your word, you'll let me tie you up.' 'There's no need,' said Richard. 'I won't do anything.'

'At least let him have a cup of tea,' said Amy.

'Just shut your fucking mouth and do as I say.'

It was the most aggressive he'd been to Amy since he first arrived.

Richard held his arms in the air and dropped to his knees.

'Face down,' ordered Billy.

Richard fell flat out on his stomach, hands behind his back.

Billy let go of Gill and began tying him up with the electric flex he'd accumulated around the cottage. He started with his hands, moving swiftly and skilfully, doubling the knots. He then did the same to Richard's ankles.

Satisfied that Richard was immobilised, Billy summoned Gill outside into what they called the dairy, but which was in fact an outbuilding. He found some old plastic clothes line and marched her back inside. When they reached the lounge, he ordered her to hold out her hands. 'Oh my god, no Billy, please,' she said.

Billy tied her hands together and directed her to sit on a stool. He then started to bind her ankles. 'What on earth are you doing. You can't tie us up, we aren't going to do anything,' said Amy. Billy told her to shut up and that she was next.

Gill began pleading. 'Please, Billy, no. Mum's been as good as gold. You gave us your word.'

Billy said he was going to take Richard's car and go, but he had to be sure they couldn't call the police as soon as he left. If anything made them feel better, it was hearing that. He tied Amy's hands behind her back, ordered her to the settee, and did the same to her ankles. Richard could only watch, numb and helpless.

At that point Arthur came into the lounge. He was horrified at the scene – all three of his loved ones tied up and looking terrified.

'Now you, pop,' said Billy.

'What the hell do you think you're doing. And who do you think you're doing it to… you're not tying me up.'

Billy grabbed the old man and hit him to the floor. Arthur landed on his shoulder with a terrible thud.

Sarah came running in and began crying. She advanced at the man, arms flailing and shouting at him that he was a bully. 'Leave him alone, leave him alone,' she cried.

Arthur still wasn't co-operating, but his resistance was restricted by his artificial leg. Billy managed to hold him down and somehow bind his hands and ankles.

Sarah, in floods of tears, ran to cuddle her father, screaming angrily at this intruder, 'don't you hurt my mummy and daddy. Don't you dare. Get out. You hurt people.'

'She's a feisty one. It must run in the family, eh pop?' said Billy.

Billy ordered the adults to the floor then disappeared. They could hear him scaling the stairs. Face down on the carpet, they turned to see him return with a handful of teacloths and towels. He began tearing them into strips.

'If anyone has false teeth, take them out.' Billy laughed at his own cruel joke. Nobody could even lift a finger.

He gagged Richard first. Then went to Amy and Arthur and pulled out their denture plates. Gill had never seen her parents without their teeth in. She wept internally at their humiliation and helplessness.

She begged, 'Please, please, don't gag mum. She's got sinusitis. She'll suffocate.' He paid no attention, winding the towelling tight around their mouths. And then he did the same to Gill, finally silencing any more pleading.

Billy manhandled Richard across to the settee. He then pulled him onto his shoulder and gave him a fireman's lift, up the stairs and into the single bed in the spare room at the far end of the corridor.

He came down and carried Gill up in the same way, but dumped her on the double bed in her bedroom. Back for a third time, he lifted Amy and put her on Sarah's bed.

But no sooner had they settled than the phone went in the hall. Sarah rushed out of the lounge, running around shouting that the phone was ringing and asking if she should answer it. Billy flew into another of his panics, ordering her to stay in the lounge and look after her grandad.

He paused as if he wanted the caller to ring off. But he suddenly raced up the stairs and ripped off Gill's gag. He then carried her downstairs to the hall. He answered the phone just in time, and put the receiver to her ear.

It was Richard's nephew, Alan Buckley, ringing from Birmingham. He wanted to speak to him. Gill said he wasn't home yet and was expected to be late. Her voice was calm and modulated, controlling the conversation whilst at the same time looking through the glass door of the lounge trying to see her father. 'I'll tell him you called.' She rang off.

Billy put the gag back on and carried her back upstairs to her room. She lay there for what seemed like an eternity. The cottage had all gone silent. She prayed he'd taken Richard's keys and fled.

In each of those three rooms the thoughts were the same, everyone hoping against hope that their nightmare was over.

The silence was shattered by Sarah. She called up the stairs, 'don't be fooled, Mum. He's being quiet. He hasn't gone yet.' Billy grabbed her and took her through to her grandparents' side of the house.

Gill wondered what was happening. Then her door opened. It was Amy. She'd somehow managed to break free from her ties. 'I think he's gone!' She was about to speak again, but saw the look of alarm on Gill's face.

She loosened her daughter's gag. 'No Mum, no… he's still here. He'll go mad if he sees you.'

With that, Amy ran back to her room. Inside, she loosely tied her ankles and wrists and put the gag over her mouth, slack enough to allow her to breathe comfortably.

However, every movement in that cottage could be heard, and Billy came racing up the stairs. He stormed in on Amy, his face contorted with anger. 'What the fuck you going?'

In temper, he yanked her gag tight again and retied her hands and ankles with deliberate roughness. She winced in pain.

Gill heard this with absolute horror. She wanted to cry out - to explain to Billy that Mum had thought he'd gone and wasn't trying to escape. But if Gill shouted out he would discover her loosened ties. She could only lay there mute.

Her emotional pain eased when she heard Amy thank Billy. He had obviously relented and slackened the wire. Then he came in and started ransacking her bedroom, almost oblivious to her presence, pulling clothes out of wardrobes and cupboards, and dumping them on the floor.

He seemed to be looking for any hidden cash. In the drawers he found clean underpants, socks, a tee shirt, and Richard's tracksuit. She turned her head away as he put them all on. He was doing everything at speed, rushing here, rushing there. Up the stairs, then down, two steps at a time.

She couldn't work out if his actions signalled that he was coming or going. Perhaps he'd reasoned that police would be looking for a man in a dark suit, not a maroon tracksuit. If he was stopped at a road check he could deny he was the escaped prisoner.

On the other hand, he seemed to be settling in for the night – asking how the central heating operated, when to feed the dogs, even the welfare of Sarah's pet rabbit. He disappeared out the room, deep in thought.

Back downstairs, he told himself he had to get control. Fucking control. And these bastards weren't making it easy for him. And he needed to do something about it. The girl was a pain in the arse, and he would sort her out later. As for the old man, there was only one solution.

Arthur was bound and gagged in the lounge chair. Blood trickled down his face and he was in obvious pain from the fall on his shoulder.

Billy took the knife from his waistband and walked towards him. He manhandled him to the floor, with Arthur now on his knees.

And for the third time that day, Billy stabbed a human being. Over. And over. And over. Through his heart, his throat, his chest. A rage of brutality.

A post mortem would later reveal that Arthur died from shock and haemorrhage, due to multiple stab wounds - so many, it was impossible to be accurate, but at least a dozen.

It wasn't so much a killing, as a cold-blooded execution, Arthur twisting and shouting, fighting for his life until he gurgled his last breath and slumped forward, blood seeping from his wounds and dripping onto the carpet.

A defenceless old man, murdered by his own knife - the one he'd used to slice meat for his customers; the one he'd honed and sharpened for years; the one this monster had stolen from the kitchen drawer.

Billy heaved the body onto the chair. Arthur's false leg fell to a grotesque angle. He tried to straighten it, but realised it had come off in the struggle. He covered the body with a blue anorak and walked out the room.

The knife was dripping with blood, but there was no point cleaning it. He had one more obstacle to remove. And she was next door in the Minton's quarters. He moved with speed to the upstairs spare room. Sarah lay trussed and frightened looking up at him. He spared her no mercy, blow after blow, long after the point that she'd died.

He returned to the Moran kitchen and calmly washed the knife in the sink, drying it on a tea towel, and putting it back in his tracksuit pocket. He secured the dividing door with clothes line, put the kettle on, and went upstairs to run a bath.

Soaking in Gill's perfumed suds, his aggression subsided. His anger became remorse. He put his head in his hands and wondered how the hell he had gotten into this state.

It all stemmed from five months previously in that long hot summer. If only he hadn't gone to Jingles that night...

20

Five months previously

Saturday August 21ˢᵗ 1976

Saturday nights at Jingles in Chesterfield were hot and wild affairs, the music deafening, the joint jumping. Lads in sleeveless vests and flared trousers eyed lasses in skimpy tops across a dance floor awash with beer. The place reeked of tobacco, sweat, and cheap scent.

Through the fug of smoke machines and John Player Specials, one girl caught the eye, giving it plenty to the Abba number one. She was no more than 20. The strobe lighting flashed across her figure as she shimmied and tossed her hair. She was tall, slim and blonde, with legs up to her armpits. Fit. And she knew it.

" … see that girl, watch that scene, dig in the Dancing Queen.."

In the shadows, Billy, half cut, took a long drag on his rollup and studied her. A few minutes ago she'd been dancing among a group of young lads. But now they were nowhere to be seen.

He'd worked that day loading and ferrying wheelbarrows full of rubble. It was thirsty work on one of the hottest days of the year.

They'd been out with Tess' brother Tony and some of his friends. At turning out time someone suggested they go on to Jingles.

Unusually, Tess had had enough and gone home. She 'allowed' him to go on the understanding that one of the party, a bloke called Stan, kept an eye on him. But Stan had met some girl and left, leaving Billy alone in a place awash with tipsy girls.

The DJ switched on the 'black' light, highlighting everything white – specks of dust, the fluff in her hair, her teeth, even the outline of her underwear through her hotpants. *Jesus fucking Christ.*

He rolled up his shirtsleeves and swaggered across in his Cuban-heels. He was small and they gave him authority and confidence.

He danced a yard away from her and moved in time with her body. She saw a man at least ten years older than her - good looking, with high cheekbones, and a mop of dark dishevelled hair. He smiled. And she smiled back.

He moved closer, wanting to touch her. He reached for her hands. She responded by raising his arms above her head and twirling under the arch she'd just created. He smiled again.

'What's yer name, love?' he shouted. 'Susan.'

'Well, Susan, you look pretty good tonight.'

He pulled her close. Within seconds they were smooching and kissing. From nowhere, this young bloke appeared flanked by a group of lads sporting bad moustaches and streaked wedged haircuts.

'Oi, pal. Clear off, she's mine.'

Billy stepped back. The girl looked embarrassed. Billy gave them the onceover. Just kids, the lot of them. He figured he could take them one by one. But they were five handed. He held his hands up as if he'd been caught by the cops and melted away into a dark corner to lick his wounds.

He had two more pints of lager, and a tequila chaser, the alcohol fuelling his resentment as he watched her smooch with her boyfriend. At 2am, the shutters went down and the main lights came on.

Outside, the Jingles clubbers joined the crowds on the street. Susan and her fella strolled off arm in arm, through the cobbled market square, towards Queen's Park, with its boating lake and county cricket pitch.

It was 2.30am on a balmy evening, officially the hottest summer for years. The moon ducked behind rolling clouds. Susan and her man stopped frequently for a kiss and a cuddle. After a mile or so, they arrived at the swimming baths on Boythorpe Road, backing onto the park. They looked around, then went around the back. They thought no-one had seen them.

An hour later, the man stumbled, dazed and bleeding, into Chesterfield's main police station in Beetwell Street. Officers listened incredulously as Richard, a 21-year-old labourer, explained how he and his girlfriend had been attacked by a madman.

He'd been knocked unconscious but didn't know what had happened to her. Saturday nights were always busy in that nick dealing with drunks and after-hours fighting. But this was something else.

They jumped in a Panda car and sped back to the scene just down the road. Behind the swimming baths, in a public toilet, they found Susan hiding and in a distressed state.

It was only in the safety of the police station over a hot drink that the 20-year-old shop assistant felt able to reveal the detail of what happened.

They'd been about to have intercourse when a man appeared out of nowhere. He'd punched Richard to the floor and grabbed her.

Richard got up, but the attacker had hit him again, this time with a brick or something, knocking him out cold.

The man had then dragged her into the park and, under the threat of violence, forced her to have sex with him. After her terrifying ordeal, he'd frogmarched her away into the darkness of the park before eventually letting her go.

Violated and confused, she'd gone to look for her boyfriend, but he was nowhere to be found. She hid in the toilets hoping he'd turn up.

The couple were taken to the nearby Royal Hospital for treatment and for forensic evidence to be gathered.

The police assigned 25 officers to the case, the most manpower for a single local crime anyone could remember. It made the front page of the local Derbyshire Times.

'A massive police hunt is on for a man who raped a 20-year-old woman and savagely assaulted her boyfriend at Boythorpe in the early hours on Sunday.

'The courting couple – they have not been named by police – were attacked without warning behind the Queen's Park Swimming Pool just after 2.30am.

'The 21-year-old man was seriously assaulted – and then the attacked turned his attentions to the woman.

'He dragged her to the bank of the River Rother, close to Boythorpe Road and raped her.

'He took her along the bed of the river into Queen's Park and out of the park at the level crossing gate on Park Road.

'The attacker was described as around 26 years. 5ft 7ins, broad build with dark brown short hair and long sideburns. He was wearing a white or cream shirt, black or dark green trousers and black shoes with Cuban heels.

'Supt. Thomas Hoggett, who is leading the hunt, warned that the man could strike again. – 'It's an unusual case. And if the offender is not caught there could be a repetition,' he said.

In the pub, one of Tess's friends joked that the description of the wanted man sounded just like her Billy. Everyone laughed, but reading the detail made her go cold.

'The attacker was described as around 26 years. 5ft 7ins, broad build with dark brown short hair and long sideburns. He was wearing a white or cream shirt, black or dark green trousers and black shoes with Cuban heels.'

It was a perfect description of her man. She was thrown into a spin. Her mind raced to the previous weekend. They'd been out to a few pubs. She'd gone home, but Billy, insisted on staying out. That was right, wasn't it?

Yes! She remembered him well-oiled at the bar. He said he'd spent many hours inside a cell. Life was for living. What time did he come in? Was she awake? No, she'd been asleep. He'd told her the next morning that he'd been in bed by one o'clock.. so it couldn't have been him! Unless, of course....

She shrugged off the description as being a coincidence. But it nagged away for the rest of that night.

She rummaged through the dirty washing basket until she found the shirt he'd worn the night of the assault. Yes, it was white. She smelt it – a mixture of male sweat and cheap perfume – the scent of a woman that definitely wasn't hers.

She examined the collar, the armpits, the back of the shirt and then, there they were.... grass stains on both elbows. She found his boxer shorts at the bottom of the basket and stared at them for a second or two. She couldn't bring herself to even touch them.

Sure, he was violent, unpredictable, and had what she termed 'funny turns,' when she knew to keep out of his way. But he was too shy, too much of a gentleman to ... well, bloody rape someone.

Besides she'd sworn never to tell anyone about his violent mood swings or that she'd once suggested he see a psychiatrist about his outbursts. Whatever her brain and her gut instinct were telling her, her heart was in denial. She'd promised herself she would change him. And this was no time to harbour doubts.

Billy had made it home in time for tea. Tess waited until they watched Coronation Street before raising the subject.

'Something's on my mind and I need to ask you,' she said.

'What's that babe?'

'At the weekend, when you stayed out drinking. Did you meet anyone?'

'What you trying to say?'

'I went to do the washing today… and.. well, your shirt stank of perfume. And it weren't mine.'

'Tess. You brush against all sorts when you're out. We have to trust each other.'

'What about the grass stains on the elbows. Where did they come from?'

Billy snapped and jumped up from the sofa. He moved inches from her face and began shouting. 'Don't you trust me?' He grabbed her around the neck. 'Let go Billy. You're hurting me.'

He threw her against the sofa and stormed out. She recovered in time to watch him from the lounge window as he walked up the street. That was the last she saw of him on the outside. He never came home.

The breakthrough came out of the blue. A local prostitute told police the man they wanted for the park rape was at her home.

'What makes you so sure?'

'He matches the description. And he wears Cuban heels whilst we're doing it. It makes him feel hard,' she confessed.

Seven policemen were sent. The woman let three of them into the house while the others covered the front and back doors. 'Where is he?'

She nodded towards the stairs. The cops searched both rooms, including the wardrobes. Nothing. Then, on the way out, one noticed an ottoman at the foot of the bed. He opened the lid.

And there was Billy, looking up like a frightened puppy. He got to his feet and meekly offered his wrists to be cuffed.

He was taken to Beetwell Street, the crumbling building that had served as Chesterfield's main nick for getting on 150 years.

Two young detectives, Bunting and Field, who'd brought him in, thought he was ready to open up. They discussed tactics – the traditional 'good cop, bad cop' routine. One would befriend him, the other would be more aggressive, in his face, even roughening the bastard up if need be.

There was added peer pressure too. The interview room was directly below the CID office. When they installed central heating, the contractors left voids in the piping duct that unintentionally became a sound funnel. Every word could be heard upstairs. Bunting handed Hughes a mug of coffee and opened a packet of newly-purchased cigarettes. 'Snout?' He hesitated, then took one.

They cautioned him and introduced themselves. Low ranking DCs. He looked at them with scorn.

Hughes admitted he'd danced with the girl and they'd enjoyed a few snogs, but her boyfriend arrived on the dancefloor and told him to back-off which he considered reasonable.

Walking home up Boythorpe Hill he'd heard laughter then saw Susan and her boyfriend go behind the swimming baths.

He paused to sip his coffee.

'Maybe I should have minded my own business…'

His voice became progressively quieter. He was almost whispering. It was the tone of someone feeling sorry for himself, wondering what had come over him that night.

'I followed them round the back and they were kissing and cuddling and that. She had her knickers around her ankles. It was obvious what they were up to.

'I said, "come on, let's be having you," half joking like, then the bloke told me to shove off.

'I jumped over the wall towards them. He started doing his flies up and come at me, so I hit him first in self-defence.

'With the drink and my Cuban heels I fell over, but as I got up I found this house brick and hit the guy over the head and he went down.

'Susan asked me to leave him alone, saying she'd do anything. Before she said that I hadn't thought of anything sexual. I asked her for a kiss and she kissed me on the lips willingly.

'At that point the boyfriend got up but I hit him again with the brick, only this time he went out cold. I said 'come with me' and she said yeah. She pulled her knickers up and we walked away holding hands. The park was locked and I lifted her over the high wall. We then lay on the grass for a while, talking.

'I said that I wanted to make love to her but she said no. I kissed and touched her and asked her again and she agreed so we did it. She was responsive.'

They'd talked for a while and then he'd seen a police car.

'For the first time, I thought of what I'd done. I said that we had to get away. She couldn't climb over the large pipe and agreed to wade across the river with me. I carried her across, stepping on stones.'

Halfway she'd asked him to put her down, so they'd walked the rest ankle-deep in water.

'We lay talking. I told her my name was Gerry and that I lived in a tent.'

They'd walked, her leading the way, him lifting her over walls and fences. At one point they'd heard a motorbike and hid in an alleyway.

'I said that she'd better go home and that I'd better go back to my tent. I went home to bed and never told a soul what happened. I want to make it clear that I used no force on her, nor threats. I accepted it when she said no, but she changed her mind and agreed. She was scared at first, but we ended up strolling and laughing like an ordinary couple.'

The officers could hardly contain their glee. Hughes had admitted he'd attacked the man, and surely, faced with such evidence, no jury would believe that she'd consented.

In the CID room where they were glued to the radiator, they rose to their feet. High-fives all around.

He was formally charged with grievous bodily harm on the man, and having had sexual intercourse with the woman without her consent, contrary to section 1(1) of the Sexual Offences Act 1956. He was put back in the police cells overnight to attend court the following day.

Around 9pm Tess called into the nick with a Marks and Spencer carrier bag containing his belongings and toiletries. 'Here. He might need these,' she said. She made no request to see him.

21

On August 27th, 1976, five days after the park rape, William Thomas Hughes, aged 30, of Boythorpe Crescent, Chesterfield, climbed from the cells into the dock.

It was another stinking day in that long, hot summer. Tarmac had melted on the roads, and landscapes were bleached pale brown. Grass looked like coconut matting.

There'd been little rain in months and fields of parched wheat caught fire. Reservoirs were barren and streams had dried up. Britain was under an Emergency Drought Act with a Government minister made responsible for handling the water shortage.

All sorts of concessions were made because of the heat. Formal clothing rules were relaxed. In court, judges allowed barristers to take off their gowns and wigs. Magistrates presided in their shirtsleeves.

The courthouse in West Bars was a futuristic building constructed in the early 1960s, all gleaming glass and shining steel, with 11 huge gables pointing to the sky. The design was so unusual the building would later be listed for its architectural interest but inside it was like an oven.

The list that day was typical magistrates fare – a potpourri of petty thieves, joyriders, fraudsters and drunks, bowing shamefully before the bench to await their fate.

Billy's hearing lasted two minutes. He stood respectfully with his head bowed, confirmed his name and address, and that he understood the charges.

No plea was taken and the three magistrates remanded him in custody to allow him to find legal representation and for both sides to prepare their case for the Crown Court trial further down the line.

Waiting in the cells to be transported to Leicester Prison, Billy underwent another mood swing. Gone was the resigned individual full of remorse and self-pity. He was now abusive and restless, patrolling up and down the cell like a caged tiger.

Up until this point he could hope this was all some ghastly dream; or that someone in the system had somehow fucked up; that it wasn't him in this mess, but an extension of his being. But deep inside of course, he knew. He KNEW what he faced in the coming weeks.

He listened to his heartbeat, examined his body over and over, prodded and poked his muscles, did countless press-ups, counted the bricks and tiles, multiplying them, then re-checking the answer by counting each and every one again.

The officer in charge was so concerned about his demeanour that he officially notified to Leicester that they were about to receive a prisoner who presented special risks – not just to others, but to himself.

He used Derbyshire Constabulary's official prison admittance Form 293 which would accompany the escort party.

It stated 'attention is called to the above prisoner who is reasonably suspected of being an exceptional risk, for one or more of the following reasons:'

likely to escape. TICK

of a violent nature TICK

having suicidal tendencies. TICK.

The duty gaoler, Police Constable Catton, followed this up with a phone call to the Reception Department at Leicester prison.

But he was left with the feeling that his call was treated more as routine than anything out of the ordinary, and that his more senior colleague's concerns had fallen on deaf ears.

Hughes spent the 50-mile journey from Chesterfield to Leicester slumped in the prison van.

He'd sufficiently calmed down by the time they arrived in the yard and obligingly held out his wrists for his cuffs to be unlocked.

The heat in reception was insufferable, the emergency fans making little difference. The desk officer was in a sleeveless shirt, unbuttoned to halfway down his chest, doing paperwork whilst listening to the Test Match from the Oval.

'Welcome to Leicester,' he said. 'Hope you enjoy your stay.' Prison officers were masters of sarcasm.

Hughes was taken to a room to be 'stripped' – prison slang for processing. Two reception officers were attended by a clerk, and a couple of prison orderlies.

'Name!' bawled the reception officer.

'Billy Hughes'

'Billy Hughes, what?'

'Billy Hughes. Just Billy Hughes.'

'Not just Billy Hughes, you stupid twat. Billy Hughes, sir! You get that?'

'Billy Hughes, sir.'

'What religion, Hughes?'

'Catholic'

'Fucking IRA-lover, eh?'

'No..'

'Don't answer me back, sonny. Scum the lot of ya. You all need topping. Empty your pockets.'

It was the usual prison greeting. Hughes had heard it all before.

He had 15 quid in notes, the keys to home, and some loose change. Some coins rolled along the desk and landed on the floor.

His carrier bag contents - two pairs of jeans, T shirts, underpants and toiletries, were itemised in a ledger.

Each article of clothing – his navy suit, white shirt, vest, underpants and socks, was meticulously recorded as it came off, and then folded by the orderlies into cardboard boxes.

Naked, Hughes walked to the scales, his weight and height were noted. He was given a minute to take a cold shower and, as a remand prisoner, allowed to wear a pair of Levi's, and a plain white sleeveless shirt.

In a room, the medical officer introduced himself as Dr Grayling. He held Hughes testicles and told him to look to the side and cough. He noted there were no signs of a hernia. Then he shone a light up his backside. On that score át least, everything was fine.

He asked the usual questions from a list of possible ailments. He noted Billy was in good physical shape.

However, Hughes made an unusually frank admission. He was, he said, liable to outbursts of aggression and violence and needed help.

They chatted. Hughes stood subdued and obedient. Grayling advised him to seek an interview with him rather than become involved in any confrontations with other inmates. He nodded.

He claimed he was not guilty of the alleged rape and wanted to buckle down whilst on remand and concentrate on proving his innocence.

Tess went to see him. He begged her to stand by him. Across the visiting table, she promised she would, but he could tell from her face it was all bullshit.

She got a friend to write to him saying she'd moved away. He wrote Tess two letters back, pleading for a second chance. She'd promised to stand by him and that was the only thing that would get him through, he wrote. But she never replied.

Twelve days after arriving at Leicester, he was escorted to Blackpool for an outstanding burglary trial. He pleaded guilty to theft and sentenced to six months.

Now, as an official guest of Her Majesty, rather than a remand prisoner, he was forced to swop his civvy casuals for prison grey.

He had now ceased to be a person. He had no one left. No wife, no girlfriend, no mother, no mates, no booze, no banter. He had nothing to read, no one to brag to, or to learn from – except of course his similarly afflicted comrades.

There were few sounds more shattering to a soul than the closing of a cell door. All at once, silence. Nothing. Inactivity. Empty time.

In normal life few minutes passed without incident or interest. In there, many hours went by in which absolutely nothing happened. He'd look at a prison clock without processing the information from it. His entombed imagination flashed out thousands of hypotheses and mixed messages that the normal mind routinely discarded.

With every hour he'd become more disorientated, blowing everything out of proportion. Little things were worried about until they became big things, the slightest worry aggravated itself to the point of obsession.

Someone once wrote that every man thrown into a cell immediately begins to live in the shadow of madness. And incarcerated after the park rape, Hughes began to crack.

22

Hughes had been granted legal aid and was represented by one of Chesterfield's oldest law firms, Messrs W and A Glossop.

They'd studied the witness statements and concluded that he had little hope of getting off. He had, after all, confessed to being there that night and attacking the young woman's boyfriend. If convicted of rape as well, he faced anything from five to ten years inside.

Three weeks into the case, his team commissioned a psychiatric report on their client. This might show that the balance of his mind was disturbed, and this could be used in mitigation to argue for a more lenient sentence, even special treatment in prison.

The assessment was carried out by a local consultant psychiatrist who worked for the North Derbyshire Health Authority.

Jonathan Stirland, in his fifties, had spent years trying to understand the complexities and workings of some of society's most troubled minds.

He'd had a distinguished career, authoring many papers, including articles for the British Journal of Psychiatry on a study of long-term patients attending a general hospital psychiatric department, and another on a comparison of subjective responses to certain drugs used by psychiatrists.

In the bowels of Chesterfield Courthouse he began reading up on Billy's background prepared for him by the defence team.

WILLIAM THOMAS HUGHES W.R.C 18043-76 C.R.O 37921-61.

William Thomas Hughes was born in Preston, Lancashire, on August 8 1946, the eldest of 6 children. His mother is Scottish, born in Dundee, who married Thomas Hughes at the end of the war.

He attended school in Preston until he was seven but he had an unsettled childhood due to his father being in the Army. His father, who was a regular solider, moved the family to Germany and there they remained for three years.

83

Thomas Hughes had found it difficult to make ends meet on squaddie pay, and the family came back. They lived at Southend on the south coast where he worked as a painter and decorator.

'But there was never enough money or job security and the Hughes family found themselves back in Army service, in Hong Kong in comparative colonial luxury, living in a large bungalow with a live-in servant.

'But with his father's health failing, Hughes returned to Britain after only a year, settling in Lancashire.

'He worked long hours and the boys began to run wild. In a sense Billy became a surrogate father, helping his mother and looking after the younger children, even cooking their meals when she was at work.

'He went to Secondary Modern School in Preston for 18 months and left school at 15. He was never academic, but defiant and hostile and often in trouble. He worked as an apprentice but was dismissed for not going to the Day Release course.

'Hughes worked with his father as a painter and decorator, but this job only lasted for one week. He then went to work as a metal polisher, but was dismissed for theft.

'Previously he had appeared at Preston Borough Juvenile Court and had received a conditional discharge for theft from unattended motor vehicles. He appeared before the same court on three further occasions and received probation, and was ordered to live in a probation hostel.

'A week after moving there he received a further sentence and was committed to a Home Office Approved School. While there he absconded five times. He was sent to Wormwood Scrubs for allocation and a comment there was made: 'immature, thoughtless little chap whose voice is just about breaking. He has been a nuisance to all who have tried to help him. Needs secure conditions and probably further education. Persistent absconder.'

The social worker there recommended that he be given the opportunity to do a vocational training course in welding at Everthorpe Borstal. But reports from there branded him a troublemaker and he failed to make the grade.

'He was given home leave but was charged with being drunk and disorderly. At the age of 19 he was released on licence only to be reconvicted a month later for shop breaking and larceny and was thus sent back to Borstal.

'During the month he lived with his parents, a family row developed because of his heavy drinking. He stated he would not return to them because they wanted nothing more to do with him.

'His father, who himself had been demoted from sergeant for taking and crashing a wagon when drunk, died last year, he thinks, of an old back injury. He was strict and close to his son until Billy started to get into trouble with the law.

'His father went to his grave having made one last attempt to get his son to go straight. He told his own boss, Arthur Carter, the full truth about his jailbird son, saying if he could only get a full-time job he was sure he would give up his life of crime.

'Mr Carter had great respect for the Hughes family. Billy's uncle was his foreman for 20 years. He agreed to take on the wayward lad as a painter.'

But it was of no use. 'Billy was lazy, sullen and contemptuous. Whenever his father tried to bring him to order, his would fly into a rage and threaten physical violence. Billy was sacked and went back to his old ways.'

'His mother, aged 49, still lives in Preston and works as a Departmental Shop manageress at Woolworths. She is a good mother, warm-hearted and they are on good terms.

'All his brothers have had trouble with the law. Three now seem to have settled down, but one is in prison for violence and theft. There is no psychiatric illness in the family.'

Stirland calculated that Billy had spent 12 of his 15 years since leaving school in penal institutions, spending what freedom he had mostly in hostels and lodging and mixing with other habitual offenders and no-hopers. His only friends were criminals.

Stirland looked for behaviour traits and indications of Hughes' personality. He read that as a 21-year-old in Risley Prison Billy began attending the Roman Catholic chapel. A report at the time stated: '… he seems ashamed of himself and there is hardly any self-respect or ambition…'

It went on to say that his prospects of successful rehabilitation were poor. He'd forfeited many days remission for eight separate disciplinary offences, including trafficking, absenting himself from prison work, fighting and bad language.

At interviews Billy himself had refused to give any guarantee that he would attempt to desist from crime. At least he was honest in that regard, thought Stirland.

Something else caught the eye. After release from Risley, within weeks he was back in court, again for burglary, and driving with excess alcohol in his blood. Standing in the dock he produced a razor blade and cut the side of his neck and wrist.

The trial was briefly postponed and Billy taken to hospital where he needed five stitches in the neck wound and four in the wrist. The court medical officer dismissed the self-harming as 'hysterical behaviour.'

There was more, much more, but Stirland had the picture. He got up from his desk and greeted Billy in the corridor where he was sitting flanked by two prison officers.

In his ideal world, this assessment would have taken place in a relaxing neutral environment, not under stark fluorescent lighting across a Formica table in a stuffy little interview room with two screws earwigging outside the open door pretending to read the Daily Mirror.

'Take a seat, Billy. Cigarette?'

Billy nodded. Stirland produced a packet of 20 from his pocket. Stirland banged his pipe out in the rubbish bin and replenished it with Old Holborn. He gave Billy a light.

Stirland scribbled in his notes that Billy was small and healthy-looking, clean and neatly dressed in a suit. His shirt was unbuttoned at the neck.

'So Billy, tell me all about yourself...'

He said his childhood was 'crap.'

He confessed to being a 'titch' at school, which made him touchy and self-conscious. He used to get into fights to prove himself. Being small at Approved School had made him aggressive and competitive, trying to be good at everything to earn approval.

Stirland was encouraged. It seemed that Billy who'd been labelled as uncooperative in the past, now wanted to open up.

Billy said he loved his children and had tried to discipline them because he thought his wife was too lax as a parent. But he regretted hitting the kids too hard. He described her as a coarse woman, given to swearing and speaking her mind, but he was still fond of her.

He said they had a good sexual relationship, but much of their troubles stemmed from his going out with other women. He admitted that when he was younger he hadn't had much of a chance to go with girls.

He said his wife had convictions for theft and wasting police time through self-inflicted wounds. She was now friendly with this woman called Alice, with whom she had convictions for theft, and who had four kids of her own.

They'd all lived in a one-bedroom flat which had done his head in, he said. It was then that he met Tess. He was fond of her, and wanted to settle down, but this was unlikely now, he said.

As for the assault at the park, he said he was shocked and scared by what he'd done.

'I've had many fights but never used a weapon and never struck anyone without reason. I don't think it would have happened without the drink inside me.'

'What about the girl, Billy?' said Stirland.

'By the end of the evening we were like an ordinary couple, strolling and laughing. I used no threats on her, and that's no word of a lie.'

Then, in the next breath he added: 'I'm afraid for the future. I enjoy the buzz I get from violence. I'm afraid I might kill someone or rape a girl.

'I'm usually a quiet, easy-going bloke, but I bottle things, have a drink, then explode. Please help me. Can I get treatment? Hypnosis, or even brain surgery?

'Surely they can cut out the aggressive part of my brain! I don't want to spend the rest of my life in prison.' With that Billy sobbed and pleaded, 'I want to see you again. There's so much I want to tell you.'

'Perhaps. But the gentlemen outside need to take you back to Leicester, Billy.' That was it. With Billy on his way back to prison, Stirland relit his pipe and talked into his recording machine for dictation.

'… *Mr Hughes was alert and coherent. There was no evidence of delusions or hallucinations. He was tense and very talkative, even from the start of our interview, seeming to be eager to unburden himself.*

Emotional responses seemed appropriate to the topic under discussion. Thus, he was remorseful at what he had done, weeping at the knowledge that he had savagely attacked an innocent man and fearful that he might in future commit even worse offences. He also wept when wondering how to approach his mother.

He repeatedly asked for treatment, suggesting hypnosis or brain surgery when the aggressive part of his brain might be cut out.

He said that he was afraid that he would continue committing crimes so that almost the whole of his life would be spent in prison.

At the end of our interview, which lasted nearly two hours, he said he wished to see me again as there was much else in his life that he wished to tell.

He admitted making a violent and unprovoked assault on the man, but considers that he did not rape the girl, but talked her into having intercourse having previously accepted her refusal.

He accepts that the girl was frightened at first but not when intercourse took place. It may be, of course that his estimation of the girl's state of fear and the events of that night are inaccurate, as he was excited and under the influence of drink; also he was reluctant to accept himself as a rapist, although he recognises his potential.

However, I think he was trying to be truthful during the interview.

Up to the age of thirteen, he had an unstable life owing to his father's frequent moves in the Army. Since the age of 15 he has led an almost exclusively criminal life.

Always competitive, with inferiority feelings due to his size, he has remained impulsive with poor self-control.

Much of his adolescence and manhood has been spent inside penal establishments with a structured external discipline that has not given him the opportunity of developing self-control.

'It is my professional opinion there is no evidence of psychosis here, nor mental sub-normality, so that Mr Hughes must be regarded fit to plead.

The nature of the present charges, and the need to protect the public, makes a further custodial sentence inevitable, but I hope this can be served in a prison where psychotherapy, perhaps on a group basis, is available.

When he is eventually discharged, a hostel would be an advantage to acclimatise him to the difficulties of a non-institutional existence.'

Stirland's five-page report was sent to Billy's solicitors but it was little use to his defence. Any hope of some miracle acquittal had vanished. More crucially, the cries of a dangerous man had gone unheeded. One that had already decided that no way would he ever be locked up again. He had to get away. To escape. Hunt down the people who'd let him down.

Society now had a very dangerous individual on its hands - a society ignorant of his catastrophic potential.

Here was an unhinged man – brooding, angry and irrational, whose pleas for help had been spurned.

A prisoner with total contempt for authority, determined never to spend another day inside.

A loner, disowned by his mother, and rejected by his wife and girlfriend.

An unstable individual who'd already displayed a determination, bordering on the sadistic, to punish and to humiliate.

A cunning criminal who had meticulously planned his escape from custody, waiting for the right time to break free, regardless of any consequences.

And, yes, a psychopath, who inexcusably had been given access to a deadly kitchen knife and who was now on the loose and a threat to anyone in his path.

23

8pm

Pottery Cottage

Unaware that this stranger had slaughtered their loved ones, Richard, Gill and Amy lay in their separate rooms, trussed, helpless, and alone.

He'd turned off all the upstairs lights. All they could do was to stare at the ceiling trying to ward off the dark thoughts invading their heads from the sounds of distress reverberating through the cottage.

Gill's bed was immediately over the lounge and she'd heard thumps and bumps and muffled cries of anguish coming up through the floorboards. And then, it had gone quiet again. She'd strained to hear something - anything - a laugh, a cry, the echo of conversation, but there'd been nothing. The silence was broken by the sound of someone running a bath.

What had he done to Dad? She was always 'daddy's girl,' and had worshipped him as a child. He'd made her dolls, built her a rabbit hutch, and through her teenage years paid for her riding and driving lessons.

He was generous and good fun, and full of fighting spirit. As a young man he'd lost a leg in a road accident but he'd never retreated or wallowed in self-pity, a quality she only fully appreciated when she became an adult herself. Instead, he bought a grocer's shop in a suburb of Birmingham. Dad and Mum had worked hard to do their best for Gill and her elder sister Barbara.

He retired north to live with her, enjoying part-time jobs as a superintendent at Tapton Pitch-and-Putt at Chesterfield, and as a caretaker at Sarah's school.

But he was a stubborn old bugger and a proud man too. She knew he would never put up with anyone ordering him around in his own home.

The door opened and the light came on. She squinted against the glare. It was Billy with a tray of teas, dressed in Richard's bathrobe and reeking of his after shave.

He untied her gag, and helped her up so she could sip from the cup he held for her. She felt pathetically grateful. He offered her a cigarette and she nodded. He lit one, held it to her mouth, and let her inhale, then repeated the action. In a quivering voice she asked, 'Where are Sarah and Dad?'

They were downstairs, he said. Sarah was next door watching TV, and pops was resting on the sofa.

'What was all that commotion?'

'You ever tried moving someone who's all tied up?' said Billy.

'But I heard him cry out.'

'He's licking his wounds. Pig-headed bastard, your dad, but he's settled down now,' he said.

He got up to deliver tea to the others, leaving her cigarette hanging over the edge of her bedside table. She could only watch as it singed the wood.

She heard the faint mumble of male voices along the corridor and then, in the next room, Mum politely appreciating the delivery of a hot drink. Gill was still sitting up when he returned some minutes later. He gently closed the door behind him.

She sensed, as a woman does, what was going to happen and knew that nothing, no amount of pleading or resistance, could stop it.

Earlier she'd felt him watching her and, waiting for Richard to come home, leering, invading her personal space, whispering in her ear. She dreaded the thought of ever being alone with him. Now there was no escape.

He laid her back down and kissed her face and neck. She turned away, trying to scream under her gag, but he pulled her cheek back into line and forcefully carried on. Then, he tore off her shirt and bra.

She stared at the ceiling as he stripped, wondering what she could possibly do to stop the inevitable.

Naked, and hovering over her, he began to untie her, first her ankles, then her hands. He then commanded her to take the rest of her clothes off, her trousers and underwear. She had no choice but to comply.

'Please,' she said. 'I've just started my period.'

It was her last tactic and he could see this was true. But, he said, there were other ways…

He climbed on top of her, kissing her aggressively and biting her neck. He then moved gradually up the bed until he was straddling her upper body. He grabbed her head and pulled it towards him. She obeyed his directions mechanically without emotion.

When it was over he was subdued. He stroked her body. She began to shiver uncontrollably. He fetched her dressing gown and tied her wrists together again, pulling the bedclothes over her to keep her warm – the only act she regarded as one of kindness.

She asked if she could use the bathroom and he agreed, undoing the knots again. He waited outside while she gargled over and over and frantically brushed her teeth.

24

9pm

Marooned in Sarah's room further along that short corridor, Richard had heard the deadened sounds of everything that had gone on in that last hour or so. And his imagination had run wild.

In the darkness, noises were always exaggerated. Had there been a fight downstairs? Had Amy broken free at some point? Had he heard Billy with Gill in their bedroom?

Billy's arrival with a drink was actually a relief. At least here was something tangible. Something real, not imagined.

Being alone and forced to lie still had allowed him time to think things through rationally and calmly. What was the best way to tackle this invasion of his home? The safety of his family were his obvious priority. He was clear about that. But how best to ensure it? He was certain it was through friendliness rather than force, which could easily backfire with alarming consequences.

Billy lifted him up, loosened the towelling around his mouth, and held the beaker to his lips. Only then Richard realised it was whisky. He sipped, blinking against the light, grateful for the aroma and immediate kick of the alcohol. 'Cheers,' he said.

Billy lit a cigarette and put it in Richard's mouth. He took a deep, welcome drag. 'What was all that racket?'

'Everyone's in separate rooms. It took a bit of muscle,' said Billy, avoiding the question.

'Where's my little girl? asked Richard.

'Asleep next door.'

'Blimey, it seems like the middle of the night. What time is it?'

'Around nine.'

'Look, I've been thinking, said Richard, 'there'll be no-one on the streets. Why don't you make a break for it?'

'I've already decided. I'm leaving tomorrow. Leave you lot in peace... assuming we all get through the night in one piece.' It was typical Hughes. Offering hope, but with a hint of menace.

'We're on your side. You know that.'

Billy said nothing. He sat on the floor, leaning against the door, smoking. He seemed relaxed. It was clear he wanted to chat.

Richard examined his wrists. His hands were blue. The flex had made imprints in his flesh. 'Christ, my hands hurt.'

Billy untied them. Richard rubbed his hands together to get the blood flowing. 'Pain is all in the mind,' said Billy.

They talked for an hour at least. Gill could hear the mumble of male voices, but not what was being said. Billy spent much of the time bragging about his strength and criminal conquests and his total disdain for the police who were as thick as planks.

Billy confessed that he'd once killed an Alsatian with his bare hands. A police dog was sent in during a factory blag and he'd no option but to silence it. 'Shame, really' he said. 'I like dogs.'

Richard's gameplan of humouring him was working, he thought. But this was a naïve, middle-class, god-fearing pacifist pitched against a street fighter of guile and cunning. Billy was playing him, not the other way around. And suddenly he seemed interested in Richard as a person.

'I bet you've always had it right easy.'

'Not at all,' Richard replied.

He told him he was born in Southern Ireland, in a tiny village called Kilmoganny, in County Kilkenney.

'I'll let you into a little secret,' said Richard.

'Yeah, what?' said Billy.

'I was illegitimate.'

'You paddy bastard!' said Billy.

Richard said his mother couldn't handle the shame and he was quietly fostered out. His new mother was called Annie - Annie Hawe.

'You what?' laughed Billy.

'Spelt with an H, not a Wh,' replied Richard.

They both smiled.

They'd been poor, but happy. He'd left school at 14 and worked as a labourer. Like all Irish teenagers he had to do National Service which was a laugh more than anything else. After that he emigrated to England penniless, doing all sorts of odd jobs. He attended five nights a week at college and worked his way up in a plastics factory.

Billy seemed taken aback and got up to go. 'Well, there you go, and there's me thinking it was all handed down on a plate,' he said.

For the rest of the night, Billy assumed the role of nightwatchman in the darkened lounge, his eyes glued to the gap in the curtains. He had his feet up on the coffee table, swigging whisky, and blowing smoke rings into the air, his trusted knife and axes by his side.

He was satisfied that at last the cottage was under control but mystified that the body of the old man just a few feet away, could still twitch and make strange sounds several hours after life had ended.

Derbyshire Police Log, Wednesday January 12ᵗʰ 1977.

10 pm message   Search operations ceased until 13.01.77.

From: Comms Room, Alfreton.

Received by: All officers on duty.

Means: Radio.

Action taken: Search to be resumed at 09.30 hours.

THURSDAY

25

8am

Thursday Jan 13th 1977

Pottery Cottage

The morning sun peered over the brow of the north Derbyshire hills, illuminating a whiteness that covered the landscape for miles. It was an idyllic scene – the stillness of a crisp winter dawn, blue skies, and the moors glistening as they awoke from their slumber.

But the surviving hostages of Pottery Cottage, alone and shackled in their rooms, were oblivious to both the horror of the previous night and the beauty of that new day.

In the lounge, Billy was woken by a thumping, mechanical sound. Was that a helicopter he could hear? He leapt to his feet and flinched against the morning light. Two Army choppers were circling. He studied them as they swept low over the moors and rose again like kites in the wind.

He scrunched newspapers and lit a fire in the grate to ensure maximum smoke to signal they were just another family waking up to another ordinary day.

He raced upstairs and burst into Gill's bedroom. She had finally got to sleep after endless hours of crying, thinking, wondering, worrying. He shook her awake and untied her.

'Get up, get up, there's something going off outside,' he said.

She used the bathroom and went downstairs in her housecoat. Billy was at the kitchen window listening to the radio news and craning his neck to the sky. 'What are those bastards up to?' he said.

'It's the Army. They do exercises all the time,' she said.

He moved towards her. She picked up the electric kettle, only to realise there was no flex, so she filled a saucepan instead. On autopilot, she went to the fridge and began pouring juice into Sarah's beaker. Billy intervened. 'What you doing?'

'It's for Sarah.'

'She's asleep in your Mum's spare room. Leave it there, I'll take it through.' he said.

'Where's dad?'

'He's asleep in the lounge. Don't disturb him. I've closed the door.'

Waiting for the water to boil, she kept quiet, anxious not to engage him or risk saying anything that might upset him or encourage his advances. The dividing door handle was still secured with flex. But was that blood? She inspected close up. The handle and the white plastic coating were stained red. She couldn't help herself. 'That looks like blood.'

Billy hardly flinched. He explained that he'd cut his hand opening a tin of salmon. He showed her his finger. It had a plaster on. He rummaged through the rubbish bin and retrieved an empty can. He held it to her face. 'A midnight snack,' he said.

'Where'd you find the plaster?' she asked.

'The bathroom cabinet,' he said.

Gill opened the fridge again. 'I need to make her a packed lunch.'

'Be sensible, Gill. She's hardly going to school today.'

'I must ring them. And we need to tell work we won't be coming in otherwise it might look suspicious.' She was now doing Billy's thinking for him.

She dialled the school number first, turning away from his stale breath as he listened beside her. She wanted to get that call over as quickly as possible. Sarah was feeling a bit under the weather, but she was sure she'd be back tomorrow, she told the school.

Gill was about to ring off but the headmistress, Miss Goodall, came to the phone and started to talk about Sarah's school work.

Sarah was in the top half of most subjects, was creative, sharp and athletic, and particularly good at sport. The previous summer she'd won a cup for sprinting. Her party trick was turning cartwheels in the playground.

The head said how pleased they were with her progress. All Gill could do was to politely agree and thank her for taking the time to talk.

She then rang work and spoke to one of the girls, saying she felt she had a cold coming on. It was Billy who disconnected the call, using his finger to cut them off. 'That's enough,' he said.

Gill went to Mum first in the spare room. Amy had been emotionally exhausted but had managed a couple of hours sleep. Gill was relieved to find that although she was tied up, she wasn't gagged. Gill gently coaxed her awake. 'Mum… mum… a cup of tea.'

Amy's face lit up. Gill held the mug to her lips and she sipped gratefully. Then reality struck home.

'Is he still here?'

'Afraid so, mum. Drink it while it's hot.'

She sipped again, and asked the time.

'Half eight,' said Gill.

'Dad's usually up by now,' said Amy.

'I've not seen him, but he's resting downstairs. I think he must have stuck up for himself and suffered for his sins,' said Gill. 'I'll make him a cuppa and see if he'll let me take it through.'

'Where's Sarah? I bet she's terrified, the poor lass.'

'Next door. He's taken her a drink through.'

'And Richard? How's he got on?'

Gill began to fill up. She turned away and put her hand to her mouth, looking at the floor. She didn't want her mother to see her upset. Amy shook her head and tried to lighten the mood. 'We're in a right old state, aren't we!' Gill assured her that everything would be fine. She had to take Richard his tea, she said.

In Sarah's room, Richard was sleepy but half awake. His mind had raced most of the night, going over his shocking homecoming, his tactics of appeasement, and that long chat with the man who'd invaded his home. The whisky hadn't helped. If anything it had stimulated his thoughts, making sleep impossible.

'Morning…,' said Gill, trying to put on a chirpy front. She began to undo his binds. 'He's still here, I take it..'

'Downstairs, thinking the Army are about to invade,' she said.

He could see the tears running down her cheeks. She stroked his face and kissed him. They hugged as if their lives depended on it.

'How did we get into this mess?' said Richard. It was half statement, half question.

There was something she needed to tell him, she said, something that had happened the previous night when the man had come into her room.

99

Quietly and matter-of-factly, she relived her ordeal. She'd rehearsed her lines, sparing him the lurid detail.

'I feel so dirty. I can't tell you the shame I feel. I'm so, so sorry...'

Richard felt sick to the stomach. He was angry, not just with Billy, but with himself. How did he not see this happening? Could he have done more? Gill was talking, but the words were going over his head. He wasn't listening anymore.

'I had no choice... I was tied up and he just forced himself on me.'

They hugged again and cried on each other's shoulder. Their tears were tinged with guilt. He repeated over and over that it wasn't her fault.

Soon it would all be over, he said, and they could put this nightmare behind them. Maybe take a short family break somewhere. Yes, said Gill, that would be nice.

Their moment was shattered by a knock at the front door. An urgent rat-tat-tat. Billy raced upstairs and burst into the bedroom.

'WHO THE FUCK IS THAT?' he said.

Gill went to the window. A council lorry was parked in the drive, its amber lights flashing. 'They've come to empty the septic tank,' she said.

'GO AND DEAL WITH THEM! Remember I've got your man here. Just act normally.'

Gill slipped her winter coat over her gown and went downstairs. She checked herself in the hall mirror and opened the door. A man in overalls was on the doorstep smiling. 'Morning,' he said.

'Oh yes, I'll be right out.'

'No need... we know the score. Besides, it's freezing out here,' he said. The man was Bobby Coles, a 45-year-old employee of North East Derbyshire District Council.

It took 15 minutes to clean out the tank. All the while, Billy kept an eye on proceedings from behind the curtains upstairs, clutching the axe. Richard was still tied up in bed.

Billy's edginess had an affect on Gill. In the state she was in, she viewed the men's appearance as a source of anxiety rather than an opportunity to raise the alarm.

When they had finished, Coles knocked on the door for her to sign the docket. She went outside to talk. One of the military helicopters flew over.

'Shall we give 'em a wave?' he joked.

The throwaway remark threw her completely.

'No… no… they'll think there's something wrong,' she said.

'Where's Arthur today?'

'Having a lie in,' said Gill.

'All right for some, eh,' he replied.

He passed her the clipboard to sign. For a moment she wavered. She could easily whisper to him to call the police. She hovered over the docket, her hands shaking. She thought about writing HELP! But what if he panicked or didn't understand? Maybe he didn't know about any escaped prisoner.

No, it was all too risky. She let the moment pass, signed her name on the bottom, and watched the men walk back to their vehicle. All prospect of blowing the whistle had gone.

Instead of going straight back inside, she went to the lounge window and put her hands against the glass to shield it from the glare. She could see Arthur slumped in an armchair, seemingly lifeless. It took her breath away. She looked back on the road. The lorry had moved on to its next appointment.

Billy appeared at the front door and shouted for her to come in. In the hall she screamed at him, 'WHAT HAVE YOU DONE TO DAD?'

She tried to go into the lounge but Billy blocked her path, manhandling her as she cried out. Over his shoulder she caught a glimpse. He was stiff and covered up to his chin. She was sure he was dead. 'LET ME SEE HIM…'

'He's fine, now let him sleep,' said Billy.

'I don't believe you, LET ME SEE HIM…'

'Let him sleep. He's had a hard time.'

Billy dragged her into the kitchen. She sat down at the table and sobbed. 'Calm down,' he said.

Almost chillingly, he made it clear that the lounge was now out of bounds and if they didn't comply 'there would be consequences.'

Over tea and toast she regained her composure. He reiterated that he was ready to leave. But he added a proviso – only if he could be certain that he wasn't going to run into a police road block.

And then he dropped a bombshell.

'Gill, I want you to drive into town to see if the coast is clear. If I'm satisfied that's the case I'll be on my way,' he said.

She took a deep breath. Still in her coat, she sat at the kitchen table and lit a cigarette. Her hands were shaking. After a few puffs she stubbed it out and went upstairs to get ready.

Billy went to Sarah's room and untied Richard's feet so he could go downstairs.

Richard rang his office, saying he'd got the flu and wouldn't be in. Billy stood next to the phone the whole time.

But unlike Gill, Richard couldn't act the part. He was offhand and brief, and the secretary sensed something was wrong. She went through to Richard's co-director David Brown saying it was unlike him to be so curt.

Within a minute the phone rang out through the cottage again. Every time this happened it sent Billy's stress levels soaring. It was David wanting to know how Richard was, and how he'd got on in Birmingham the previous day.

Richard put on a poorly voice and said the meeting had been successful and he would brief everyone as soon as he was back in the office.

Richard rang off, and the phone sounded again. This time it was one of Gill's colleagues, Sue Silkstone, enquiring about her health. Richard said the first thing that came into his head. It was 'woman's troubles' and his wife would no doubt be back tomorrow.

Gill appeared in the hall in her winter coat and boots and fully made up. Richard was astonished. 'Where you going?'

'He wants me to run an errand, get some cigarettes and a paper and see if there are any police about.' Billy nipped upstairs.

'What will you do if you see the police?' Richard whispered.

Gill looked him in the eye. 'I think he's done something to dad. We can't risk it, Richard.' 'But…' He could hear Billy coming downstairs.

Hughes handed Gill a pound. 'A leaving present from the screws.'

And then the tone changed. Richard would be bound and gagged upstairs while she was out. She'd better hope that no-one came because he would get it.

Gill grabbed her car keys and left the house. She could see Billy watching her from his favourite spot, behind the lounge window curtains.

With the property secure, Richard tied up again, and Gill out of the way, Billy moved quickly. He dragged Arthur's body further along the lounge, under the archway, and into the dining section. He dumped it just inside the dining room hidden from view from the lounge door, and covered it over.

Gill took her scouting mission seriously, watching intently for road blocks, and repeatedly checking her rear mirror. In her scrambled mind, the police were her enemy too. Every car could be an unmarked police car. Every person, an officer in plain clothes.

She drove several miles along the main Chatsworth Road until she reached Brampton, an urban sprawl on the outskirts of Chesterfield, famous locally for the 'Brampton mile pub crawl' a survival race to drink in each public house.

The road home was straight, around three miles. At Parsons Newsagents she queued for what seemed hours. *Was everyone watching her? Did they* <u>*know?*</u> Following Billy's orders, she asked for three national newspapers and 40 John Player Special and prayed the server wouldn't engage in small talk about the escaped prisoner or ask questions about the need for three different newspapers.

Mindful of Billy's instructions, she made a detour to assess police activity. She drove FURTHER into town, and turned right at the island to go along Boythorpe Road. This took her past Queen's Park, where Billy had committed the rape, and the road where he'd lodged with Tess. She turned right again as far as Walton Road where she completed the circle by heading back to the A619 Chatsworth Road.

But instead of heading straight home, she took another detour, this time to the village of Holymoorside. Not once did she see any police activity nor encounter a road check.

She put her foot down and headed home. Pulling into the drive, she felt relieved - and rather pleased with herself.

Billy, who'd watched her arrive back, was lurking in the lounge doorway. He grilled her about the cops.

'It's all clear, Billy. You'll be fine.'

She peered over his shoulder and realised that Arthur was no longer there.

'Where's Dad?'

'He's gone through for a kip. Said he preferred his own bed. He's next door with Sarah.'

In that split-second Gill felt massive relief. There was no way Billy could have lifted a deceased 15-stone man all the way from the lounge, through the kitchen to his home and then up their stairs.

She must have been mistaken thinking he was dead. From then on, she embraced the hope that he was alive.

What about Sarah? She HAD to see Sarah.

26

Derbyshire Police Log, Wednesday January 12th 1977.

10.58pm… message: 'I've just come home from work and my wife says she heard a prowler round the back of the house.'

From: member of public, Chesterfield.

Received by: Comms Room, Chesterfield West.

Means: Telephone.

Action taken: Officer and dog handler to scene.

Outcome: Negative.

It had been a frustrating night for Derbyshire Police. The road checks and searches had been abandoned for the day, but that hadn't stopped the public dialling 999 with supposed sightings of Hughes.

Every hitchhiker, every open gate, every stranger on a street seemed to have been reported. And every call had to be checked out. Nothing. Two hundred and fifty premises searched. Again, nothing. It had been 24 hours. Hundreds of manhours. Not a sniff.

An unmarked police car had camped outside Tess's home in Chesterfield all night, and Hughes' wife and child had been moved to a safe location in Blackpool in case he had somehow slipped the net and travelled there.

Chief Inspector Howse had been contacted by the officer in charge of an Army Air Corps unit at Farnborough in Hampshire. His pilots had been deployed to the Peaks on a training exercise but had been forced to cancel because of impending bad weather. Would he like use of two of their helicopters?

Howse was thrilled at the offer. By abandoning the car in such an isolated spot, Hughes had in fact made his re-capture more difficult. Rather than linear miles of road, he'd brought into play hundreds of square miles of moorland as well. Searching the moors on foot was not only treacherous, but would require a huge injection of police manpower – resources he just didn't have.

Howse planned to send two of his men up with the pilots. But he didn't get the favourable response he expected. Mitchell was worried about the safety implications and who'd be liable in the event of a crash. Through gritted teeth, Howse explained that since they were Army helicopters, passengers would be automatically insured by the Ministry of Defence, the Government, even the bloody Crown.

So at first light, Sergeant Clement and Sergeant Major Thwaites, of the 664 Parachute Squadron, had taken to the skies. They were accompanied by Detective Constable Burton and Constable Yates, two local police officers, who each had an OS map and were in radio contact with Howse on the ground. Their silhouettes looked like giant insects on the snow as they hovered above.

The men were briefed to fly a tight radius of the search area, checking on out-buildings for any signs of life on the moors such as fresh tracks in the snow. The Westland Lynx copters were versatile aircraft used extensively to patrol the so-called Border Country in Northern Ireland during The Troubles. They were ideal for the undulating terrain of the Peak District.

But from their bird's eye view, the officers saw nothing to arouse suspicion, just mile upon mile of white sparkling moorland unbroken except for a checker-board tracing of grey stone walls.

On the moorland roads, it was just another rush-hour – the usual line of cars, vans and lorries for once with no need for headlights. The only real activity was a council sanitation vehicle emptying septic tanks. They'd watched as a woman chatted to the workmen on the drive of a cottage, but everything had seemed normal.

'Diddly squat, guv,' as one of the men radioed back.

Mindful of the approaching blizzard, Howse called it a day, and the aircraft went home.

Mitchell summoned his senior officers to the crash scene to review tactics. The abandoned taxi had been taken away for forensic examination, but the Assistant Chief Constable wanted to see the location for himself. Dressed in hi-vis yellow jackets, and wellington boots, they gathered with maps and latest search reports.

Privately, senior officers began to fear the worst. Maybe they'd missed something, that somewhere out there a family were being held against their will by a desperate and dangerous man.

Since daybreak, another 112 buildings had been searched and 204 officers deployed, visiting farms and outbuildings and manning road blocks.

Looking out over the bleak moors, Mitchell became more convinced than ever that their strategy was correct. To the north, towards Eastmoor and south, towards Matlock, was difficult open terrain, deep ruts which were boggy, rocky escarpments, and snow drifts. There were many hillocks and no immediate concealment except by lying in the uneven ground. No, he and his team had been right all along.

He reaffirmed that Hughes was most likely in the area - somewhere in the two and a half miles between where the car was abandoned and the A6. He reiterated his instructions - all houses to be properly searched; all out-buildings be properly searched; and that all isolated places in a radius around the area be visited. This would not, of course, have included Eastmoor, completely in the wrong direction.

He was mindful too that to search a building properly took a small body of men and several hours of time. It was a huge drain on resources. And everyone was aware that the blizzard closing in was likely to make further searches virtually impossible.

CHES VEGAS,' as its detractors called Chesterfield, was a quirky town, defined by a crooked spire on its 14th century town centre church. Detractors in Derby to the south, and Sheffield to the north, quipped that only when a virgin finally married there, would the spire magically straighten.

The town had a grand history. After King John granted it market status in 1204, it had become a prosperous, bustling centre, attracting the wealthy and landed gentry.

By the mid 1970s, those affluent days had gone. Sure, local factories still churned out nappies and beer glasses for markets home and abroad, but the town battled against a general economic downturn.

However, the canal and rivers still flowed; the centre stores maintained their Mock Tudor frontages; the huge cobbled market was packed every Thursday; the 'Spireites' forever languished in the nether regions of the Football League; businessmen piled on the Master Cutler

107

train every day to go to London; and the Derbyshire Times came out every Friday.

It was a respected family-owned publication, dating back over a century, with editions throughout the Peak District and a circulation of hundreds of thousands - one of the highest in the country. Births, deaths and marriages, golden weddings, 100th birthdays, Women's' Institute events, and court proceedings were reported alongside pit strikes, factory closures and local sporting success.

So news that a dangerous prisoner was at loose was a big deal for all editions. The problem editorially was that the story had broken on a Wednesday and they had a Thursday afternoon deadline. It was all across the local dailies and on local radio. The local paper needed its own fresh angle.

The journalists were old school, with good contacts, and trusted to keep confidences. Reporters Alex Leys, Tony Whiting and Barrie Farnsworth hit the phones, chatting to police officers. At midday, they began typing the front-page lead for tomorrow's edition....

Three major possibilities were being studied yesterday by top police officers leading the manhunt for the dangerous armed prisoner who fought his way to freedom with a knife in a hi-jacked taxi.

And yesterday morning, police called in two Army helicopters to carry out low-level probes over the snow-covered moorlands at Holymoorside and Beeley.

THEORY ONE is that the 30-year-old man is holding a family hostage in an isolated house on the moors.

THEORY TWO is that the man could be suffering from exposure or even be dead after a night on the snow-covered moors when temperatures plunged to seven degrees below.

THEORY THREE is that the man has broken out of the police ring stretching from Matlock to Baslow and Chesterfield – a ring that was thrown around the area within 45 minutes after the man made his escape at 10am on Wednesday.

A top police officer told our reporters at noon yesterday, 'we are keeping a very open mind on all these possibilities. We cannot discount any of them. We are really concerned for the protection of the public. This man is dangerous and may be violent. We are warning everybody not to have a go. Leave this man to us.'

27

2.30pm

Pottery Cottage

Hughes scoured the national newspapers for news of his escape. 'Not a thing,' he said, throwing the Daily Mirror to the floor in disgust. He couldn't understand how he wasn't national news. It was obvious the screws hadn't died, he figured.

Gill made coffee for the adults and a Ribena blackcurrant for Sarah.

'Let me take it through. She'll be worried sick that I've not been in to see her,' Gill pleaded.

But she was banging her head against the wall. He insisted with that same intensive, threatening glare, that it was his job and his alone.

She just couldn't risk his wrath by arguing the point.

She went upstairs. She could hear her mother's strangled breathing from the hall and found her gagged tightly, her hands tied in front.

She was a pitiful sight. White, with bags under her eyes, and looking frail. She'd aged years in a few hours. Her hands were blue and swollen, her eyes shot with blood. Gill loosened the tea towel. Amy sipped with quivering hands.

Gill felt helpless. All she could do was again reassure her mother that they'd survived the worst and that it would soon be over.

'Don't worry, love. We're made of good stock, our lot,' said Amy. She spoke in a quiet voice, barely audible. She couldn't believe he'd allowed Gill to go out on her own. 'Did you see anyone?' Meaning, of course, the police. 'No Mum.'

She said she was more concerned in making sure the roads were clear for when he left in a few hours.

Amy clasped the mug and looked at her daughter plaintively. 'What about Dad? I've asked to go and see him but he won't let me,' she said.

Gill sat on the edge of the bed and cuddled her.

'Same here,' said Gill.

'Do you think something's happened to him?' Amy asked.

'I think he just wants to keep him out of the way,' said Gill.

'And what about Sarah, Gill?'

Gill couldn't manage a reply.

She kissed her mother's forehead, and went in to see Richard. His arms were bound as well as his hands – the price for being Billy's insurance policy in case Gill contacted the police on her trip. She thought he was bearing up well, considering all that had gone off.

'How did you get on?' said Richard. 'Fine,' she said.

He wanted to ask if she'd alerted the police but it was obvious the answer was no. He put her feelings above everything. Now wasn't the time to fight. She was right, he said. They had to play along with him.

'He wants me to go with him,' muttered Richard.

'It'll work out fine. Just do as he says,' said Gill. She kissed him and went downstairs.

Billy was buzzing around, looking out the windows, darting between rooms.

'Is there any need to keep everyone tied up?' Gill begged. 'Surely you trust us by now.'

He stopped in his tracks and moved in close. He grabbed her, fondled her bottom, and kissed her neck. How she hated these moments alone. 'I've some news,' he said.

There was a pause, a deliberate dramatic moment to leave her hanging and expectant. 'I'm leaving.' 'When?'

'As soon as I can get my things together. I'm taking Richard's car. He'll have to come with me, but I can drop him off somewhere and he can make his own way back.'

'There's something I want before I go, though.'

Billy smiled. That same leering look. And for the second time in 12 hours she knew what was about to happen. She had learned quickly how he operated. He'd made a concession - and she now had to pay for it. He led her upstairs and told her to lie on her bed.

She pleaded, but he was in no mood to negotiate, forcing her down on the mattress as she shook her head from side to side. He tied her hands and ankles and sat on the bed looking at her.

'Where's Sarah, Billy? Assure me you wouldn't want to hurt her.' It was a desperate attempt to salvage something from what was ahead.

'She's all right, Gill.' He was using her name all the time now. 'I've got a little girl of my own.'

As he spoke, he started to undress. All the clothes were Richard's – tracksuit, T shirt, even underpants. Now naked, he untied her, and told her to take all her clothes off. He made her repeat the same sex act as before – the same force, the same total disregard, the same ending.

Gill Moran got through it as she had the first time, pretending it wasn't happening to her, but to some other being in her imagination. She had stepped outside herself.

Satisfied, he got dressed. The knife he carried everywhere fell to the floor. She was shivering again so he allowed her to put her clothes on. For some reason he didn't insist on tying her up.

He went next door to Richard. She could hear them talking but couldn't make out what they were saying.

She used the bathroom and by the time she got downstairs, Richard was on the kitchen floor leaning against the sink unit. His hands and feet were tied.

Billy smiled at her. 'There's been a change of plan,' he said. 'I'm not taking Richard anymore…

'What do you mean?'

'…I'm taking you.'

Gill began shaking uncontrollably.

Richard spoke up. 'Billy, please. Gill's been through enough. Stick to your first plan. I'll come with you.'

Billy went to the lounge and came back with a bottle of whisky.

'This is to celebrate my departure … and to calm your nerves,' he said. He poured them both a glass and untied them.

He fetched Sarah's pink beaker from the cupboard and poured himself a large measure. They bit their lips.

He said it was unfair to leave Mum out, and they all went upstairs taking the bottle, their drinks, and a fresh glass for Amy.

'Here you go. A farewell drink,' he said, untying her and filling her glass. She wondered what on earth was happening.

'As soon as I've got everything together, I'm off,' Billy said, adding, 'in the meantime, let's play cards!' Richard said he would fetch a pack.

'Be quick.'

Gill, Billy and Richard played rummy on the bed, with Amy keeping score. The alcohol made them relax and they even joked about cheating

111

and argued amicably about whether she was recording the scores accurately.

After a few games Billy said he was bored of rummy and would teach them a game called Chinese Patience. They played for half an hour or so with Billy insisting they play for money.

Gill said the drink had made her hungry and suggested she prepare something. Billy was happy to allow them all to follow her to the kitchen untied.

She defrosted some meat and made everyone burgers, chips and tomatoes – six platefuls. Billy again insisted only he take Sarah and Arthur's food through.

The four of them sat at the table. They ate in almost total silence. Although Billy had snacked on and off, this was the first time any of the others could stomach anything.

It was an indication of their newfound optimism that they all cleared their plates. Afterwards, Billy let the dogs in and took Gill outside to feed the rabbit.

Amy began washing up and Billy went next door to fetch their dirty plates, untying and securing the dividing door there and back. They noticed that while all the food on Sarah's plate was gone, Arthur's was untouched. 'It's because he hasn't got his teeth in,' said Amy.

Gill asked Billy if Dad could have his teeth and a bar of Galaxy chocolate, his favourite snack. Billy agreed and took them through, joking that it was like being a bloody waiter. The cards, gambling, whisky and meal, were a welcome distraction. But they diverted everyone's attention from what was happening in the real world outside.

It had begun with a few specks of snow, then many flakes settling on the ground. Then came a howling wind, whipping drifts across the moors as a blizzard moved at frantic pace from the east. Its speed took everyone by surprise. By chance Billy peered out to the drive. It was under a thick covering of snow. Even if his intention of leaving the cottage that evening was real, the weather had cruelly wrecked any hope of him going in the foreseeable future.

Gill, Richard and Amy joined him at the window. And their hearts sank.

Derbyshire Police Log, Thursday January 13th 1977.

3.34pm… Owing to severe weather conditions, heavy snow, all mobiles recalled to sub-HQ.

From: Supt Barratt
Received by: All mobiles
Means: Radio.

Derbyshire Police Log, Thursday January 13th 1977.

4.58pm … All police cars are to be withdrawn from patrol and only to be used for essential journeys until further notice.

From: Comms Room, Chesterfield West.
Received by: Teleprinter.
Means: Radio.

28

8pm

As the name suggests, the Highwayman Inn, a hundred yards along the A619 from Pottery Cottage, had a colourful history. The rich and the famous had rolled that road, on their way to Chatsworth - kings and queens, Prime Ministers, aristocrats, foreign dignitaries, even US presidents.

Navigating the Peak District was once fraught with hazard from gangs of robbers and masked highwaymen. Notorious criminals such as Black Harry, 'Swift Nick' Nevison, and old man Pym, preyed on packhorse trains.

Centuries later, around the coal fire and at the bar, the name of a modern-day highwayman, William Thomas Hughes, was on everyone's lips.

It was a thin crowd that night. The weather meant that only a few hardy souls ventured out. Every time the door opened they stared to check out who it was – just in case.

In that context, it was no real surprise when two frozen bobbies in Hi-Vis yellow jackets and wellingtons, walked in from the cold.

A woman living near Pottery Cottage had phoned 999 reporting that a stranger answering Hughes' description had knocked at her door asking for directions to Chesterfield. He'd gone away, but later returned, insisting on being told the way and had become abusive.

Even though police vehicles were grounded, the police were obliged to check this out. It was arranged for a police Panda car to track a snow plough down to her home near the Highwayman Inn.

The officers flashed a photo of Hughes around the bar. Had anyone seen him? Everyone shrugged. The PC's thanked them and said their goodbyes. They had to knock on a few doors.

Outside the pub they chatted about what to do next. It was dark and cold, and the road was rutted with snow. They could see a cottage just along the road and debated whether or not to walk down and check it out. But it looked snug and secure. Smoke billowed from the chimney, its lights glittered across the snow, and there was a car on the drive.

Everything looked in order. So they decided not to bother. They radioed in. Mission completed.

Inside that cottage, their man was rushing around with the transistor radio. Each hour Radio Hallam reported the same line – 'bad weather has forced police to call it a day in their search for the escaped convict Billy Hughes…'

'That's great Billy', said Gill. 'It's a good time to go.' But he didn't believe it. It could be a trick. He said he wanted a 'trial run,' taking Richard and Gill with him to see for himself.

Hughes changed into his suit and took Amy back upstairs. For the umpteenth time he tied her up. He was pretty efficient by now, the whole operation performed in less than a minute. But this time he secured her with double knots.

He called the dogs upstairs and put them in with her and left all three locked in the room with bowls of water.

Richard's car was covered in snow. Billy and Gill swept it off, while Richard cleared the drive. He then got behind the wheel, with Billy beside him, and Gill in the back.

Billy switched the radio on and turned up the volume.

The Chrysler started first time and slid out onto the road. Billy hadn't a clue where they were, but had studied Arthur's map book and directed Richard to head for Chesterfield.

Within minutes it began to snow again. The roads had been partially cleared, but the new fall settled fast and the car skidded and slithered. Even with Richard's skills as a rally driver, things became impossible. Billy said it was no use, and ordered Richard to turn back. The Morans felt like weeping.

They left the car in the drive and went inside. Gill made a cup of tea and went upstairs to Amy. Billy was already there, untying her.

The poor woman looked rough. She was baffled at what was going on and kept asking questions which Billy ignored.

Richard came in. Hughes said he would have to tie him up again until he figured things out. In this mood he appeared friendly, almost apologetical.

They considered it a good moment to gently question him. Amy asked about Arthur. Gill asked about Sarah. Richard chipped in when necessary.

'They're fine. They're enjoying themselves watching telly and reading.' He'd had to tie Sarah up, but it was only with a pair of tights. Arthur's hands were tied at the front. Neither was gagged.

'Then why hasn't she cried out?' begged Gill.

'Because I've told her not to… she's a good little girl, you must be proud of her. Don't be angry, but I told her she must stay in the room, not open the door, and not make any noise, because if you do, bad things will happen to your mummy and daddy.

'And because she loves you so much, she's keeping as quite as a mouse. She's doing it for you.'

Gill looked across the room and saw Sarah's grey elephant she used as a comforter. 'I'm surprised she hasn't asked for Jumbo. She can't sleep without him.'

'Well, she hasn't,' Billy said.

'Let me take it through. Put my mind at rest,' she said.

Billy's eyes flashed.

'Are you calling me a liar?'

'No… it's just I want to see for myself that she's all right. It's only natural, Billy. I'm her mother.'

Billy went to his inside pocket and produced a photograph of himself with his young daughter.

'I've one of my own. How could I hurt Sarah?'

Then he said if it helped, he would take the comforter to her. He picked Jumbo up and went downstairs. They could hear him moving around next door. He returned a minute or so later.

'You were right. You should have seen her little face,' he said.

Gill pictured Sarah's eyes lighting up. And a wave of comfort swept over her. And she believed him. How could a father ever hurt another child?

Billy went to the window. The snow had stopped. A snowplough trudged by, its amber lights flashing in the night sky.

And then he revealed the real reason for the aborted journey earlier. He'd done a job with another man but was arrested and was owed his share of the haul. He said he needed to collect some money that was owed to him.

'Where from?' Richard asked.

'Sutton-in-Ashfield,' said Billy.

116

'Blimey, that's a good hour from here,' said Richard. 'I can drive you over. When you've collected the money, just take the car, leave me there and I'll make my own way back.'

Billy stroked his chin like a man with a lot on his mind. He went to Gill's bedroom. From the landing, Gill noticed him in her bedroom packing things into Richard's grey suitcase, workmanlike and deep in thought.

He'd been in and out of Richard's clothes all the time and she wondered what he was going to take with him. She was determined to stay out of the way, but curiosity got the better of her and she went inside and asked him what he was doing.

'Getting ready to go.'

Gill went along the corridor to tell the others. Tears rolled down Amy's cheeks and Richard looked to the heavens and thanked the Lord.

Gill moved back to her bedroom with the intention of jollying him along. But she was staggered to see him wearing her brown wig. He was at the dressing table adjusting it in the mirror.

'Not even my Mum would recognise me in this,' he said.

Her attention turned to a carrier bag on the bed. She looked inside. There were her shoes, a necklace, her underwear, a couple of tops, and a packet of tampons. It took a second or two for the awful truth to dawn. *He was taking her with him!*

He rose from the dressing table and walked towards her. A frisson of fear ran through her. He ran his hands over her, held her, and caressed her and told her she was attractive.

'I've packed you some spare undies. You need to get ready,' he said.

She pleaded with him that he didn't need her. She would only get in the way, something else for him to think about. But he became agitated. It was always like dealing with an unexploded bomb. And rather than risk another explosion she backed off.

He grabbed the suitcase, the carrier bag, Richard's sweater and one of his suits, and dumped them in the hall downstairs. He went back up to Sarah's room to secure Richard and Amy with wire. She was on the bed, Richard leaning against the wall.

He didn't pull the knots tight, but made sure there were plenty of small knots so that they couldn't escape. From the dresser on the landing he got a jug and two glasses and filled them with water from the bathroom and left them on the floor.

'Give me three hours. I'll leave her by the roadside and the police will bring her back,' he said. He smiled and closed the door.

Gill waited in the downstairs hall. He came down in her chic wig, wearing her yellow fine-leather gloves – she'd bought them for her honeymoon 17 years previously - and one of her winter coats. He might have passed for a woman if it wasn't for his Cuban heeled boots. She had to suppress a giggle.

Before leaving there was one other job – to feed the Sarah's rabbit and he disappeared outside.

With freakish timing, the phone rang. Billy came rushing back. 'Answer it!' he demanded.

It was Keith Bradshaw, a colleague of Richard's. He wanted to talk. Is Richard feeling any better? Had they heard about the loony on the loose?

Billy, who was listening, stiffened at the word 'loony' and Gill saw the same vicious expression which had frightened her so much before. She couldn't wait to get off the phone, throwing out an excuse to Keith that someone was at the door.

As soon as she put down the receiver, Billy ripped the wires from the wall.

'The bastard. I'm not having that… a fucking loony he called me. Who does he think he is?'

She tried to soothe him – 'we all know that's not true. The police have probably put that out to frighten everyone.' She tried to calm him down. 'We'd better go,' she said.

Outside, it had stopped snowing. Billy threw everything onto the back seat of Richard's car. Gill reversed out while Billy stood in the road to make sure it was safe.

But the Chrysler stalled in the gateway and got stuck. She turned the ignition again, revved the engine, but the wheels just spun without traction. Billy bumped it from the front – and the car reversed dramatically out of the drive.

He ran to the road, jumped in the driver's seat and she slid across allowing him to take the wheel.

The roads were passable but hazardous. They travelled with the radio blaring and a whisky bottle between them. It was like a scene from a Hollywood gangster movie.

With one hand on the wheel, he grabbed two cigarettes from the packet and put them in his mouth. He lit them at the same time and passed one to Gill.

He spent the journey telling the same stories – boasts about how he was a master burglar and an expert at slitting throats. He knew how to do this so that a man wouldn't die, to maim not kill,.. although he knew how to kill if he really wanted to, he said.

What she didn't know was that hidden down beside him was his knife.

The market town of Sutton-in-Ashfield was 20 miles away, off junction 28 of the M1, over the border in Nottinghamshire. But just as they entered the motorway, Billy swore and said he'd forgotten some letters with the address. They would have to go back.

It was the opposite of everything she had braced herself for – 'You can't have… YOU CAN'T HAVE!'

She reached over to the back seat, opening the case, scattering everything. They pulled up and she made a more thorough search at the side of the road, but the letters were nowhere to be found.

She sobbed. 'Why don't you get out and leave me with the car? It will take me an hour to get back by which time you'd be long gone.'

'I'll think about it,' he said.

Gill calmed down and they drove in silence. But as they crept closer to home, she became more and more worried – not just thinking about the fate of Sarah and Dad – but petrified that Richard and Mum might have somehow broken free and that he would discover them.

'If Richard and Mum have broken free, it's only because they want to see Sarah and Dad. It won't be to call the police,' she said.

Approaching the cottage, Gill had a brainwave. She suggested she dash inside to fetch the letters while he turned the car around. But Billy was having none of it.

'Don't take me for a mug,' he said.

He pulled up in the drive and got out, taking the keys with him and ordering her to stay in the car.

The next two minutes were agony. She was shaking and swigging whisky. He suddenly appeared back at the car ready to go. She assumed he'd found the letters, but didn't dare ask.

Back on the road, with the music blaring, he appeared calm. He repeated – it must have been for the third or fourth time since his arrival - his boasts about his criminal career. It was if she was a moll he'd just met in some dodgy club that he wanted to impress.

He speculated about his chances of escape. They were good, he said, because he was so skilful. He was used to being on the run, you needed to be tough and ruthless to succeed.

The way he was talking, she feared he was about to dump her on some snowy roadside verge in sub-zero temperatures.

'Billy, you know we've played it straight with you, that we're on your side. When you get this money why not leave me the car? You're clever, you can easily get another one. We'll find a car-park somewhere.

He looked at her, his cigarette in the corner of his mouth, and laughed scornfully.

'I'll just hijack a car and take the driver with me. I'm afraid of no-one.' People were stupid. They never locked their car doors. He would wait at traffic lights and just jump in.

On the outskirts of Sutton-in-Ashfield, he asked her to keep an eye out for Ron's Café. It was the rendezvous point with the man who owed him money.

He pulled up halfway on the pavement and produced a scrap of paper from his inside jacket pocket. It was a hand-drawn map. There was a little square off Huthwaite Road, with spidery handwriting 'café.' It looked like a kid's map of Treasure Island, with X marking the spot where the gold was buried.

Gill thought it a better idea if she took the wheel, so that he could concentrate on the whereabouts of the café. He got out and walked around. A determined and brave soul might have quickly seized the wheel and sped away, but she meekly slid across to the driving seat.

As they cruised the street, his mind was now entirely on the map, eyes up and down from the road, cursing that he couldn't find it. He said it was near a cemetery, but finding a cemetery in the dark was nigh on impossible.

He ordered her to stop the car. The café was there, across the road. However it didn't have a sign 'Ron's Café' as she expected. And it was pitch black, with the shutters down.

It was well after midnight, and the street was deserted. A hundred questions raced through her mind about what was going on, but she kept quiet and waited for him to decide what to do.

He took the keys out of the ignition and jumped out, telling her to wait in the car. She lit a cigarette and stared at the frontage of the café across the road. Billy disappeared into the darkness.

She waited. And waited. Cigarette after cigarette. She began to get cold, particularly her feet, which she couldn't now feel.

All sorts of thoughts went through her head. Should she try to escape? She could easily find a house and knock at the door. But what if he was testing her loyalty, hiding behind a wall watching her? What if he had indeed hi-jacked another car and abandoned her an hour from home? What would she do if a police car came along?

Was this all some elaborate ploy that she just couldn't figure out? Perhaps he was chatting in the café... but the place was in darkness.

Every time she came up with an idea, it was immediately trumped by her determination to hang on in there; that it would soon be over; that in the very next scene of this B-movie he would be on his way. Oh how she cherished normality, to be an ordinary family again.

Billy appeared at the driver's door agitated. He was sweating and breathless.

'Quick, quick, open the fucking the door,' he shouted.

'You've got the keys, not me,' she yelled.

He jumped in and fumbled around in his pockets. He was carrying what looked like a policeman's truncheon which he tossed in her lap.

He found the keys and pulled away, the tyres screeching and slithering across the tarmac.

'Bloody hell. I think I might have done him in. I was

waiting at the back door when this copper appeared from nowhere with a truncheon.

'What?'

They were now racing away, 50mph in a 30mph zone, Billy constantly checking the rearview mirror. She found herself looking back too. For what, she didn't know.

Billy said he'd headbutted him, snatched the truncheon, and smashed him over the head with it. He was out cold, his face in the snow. He'd legged it and had never got to see his friend nor the money.

'I just hope that copper's all right, or we're both in trouble. If he comes round in the next five minutes we've had it. They'll be cops all over the place,' he said.

'WE!!??'

'You're my accomplice, accessory before the fact. Like Bonny and fucking Clyde,' he laughed manically.

Gill was white with fear. He offered her a swig of whisky. She declined. He was getting a kick out of her gullibility.

As they put miles between themselves and the café, Billy progressively calmed. He drove within the speed limit, happily singing along to the radio.

Gill was in turmoil, wondering about the fate of the copper.

What she didn't know was that the story was a load of bull. The back door of the café had been left unlocked for the cleaners. Billy had just walked in. The truncheon was hanging on the wall, presumably to be used against intruders or even as a bizarre memento.

But the whole episode served its purpose – to plant more fear and anxiety into Gill's already fragile state of mind.

After a few minutes, she felt composed enough to speak.

'I've been thinking, Billy… it would be nice if Sarah could spend the night with me.'

He looked across with those blank, dead eyes, a cigarette wedged in the corner of his mouth.

He knew why Gill didn't want to sleep alone.

He switched his eyes to the road and stayed quiet.

FRIDAY

29

2am

Billy pulled into the drive with the arrogance of a boy racer, showing total disregard for the conditions. The car slid into a mound of snow and cut out. He turned the engine over and over but it wouldn't start.

'Bollocks, I think I've flooded it,' he said.

He left the Chrysler skewed at an angle.

They went straight upstairs. Mum and Richard were awake, and still tied up. Richard looked at Gill with pleading, enquiring eyes. 'I'll explain later,' she whispered.

Billy showed them the truncheon.

'Where on earth did you get that?' said Amy.

Gill went downstairs to make everyone a cup of coffee. The heating was off, and she was still in her coat. She wrapped her hands around the mug to warm her fingers. Billy came in and cuddled up to her from behind.

'Billy, please let Sarah spend the night with me,' she begged.

'No, leave things as they are,' he replied.

'Please Billy......'

He released his grip.

'For fuck's sake. Don't keep hassling me. I've told you enough times....'

Gill ran at the dividing door. It was secure but she desperately tried to open it.

He moved to the door and dragged her back. She began crying.

'I WANT MY DAUGHTER. I WANT TO SEE HER. WHERE IS SHE?'

The tears were running down her face. 'What do you care about people? You say you've got a child, you love children, but you don't care about anyone's feelings. You don't, you just don't.'

He was angry, throwing things around the kitchen. They could hear the echo of smashed crockery upstairs.

His outburst shocked her to stop crying. It was as if he'd turned off a tap. There was anger and hate in his face.

'I'm sorry Billy. I'm sorry,' she sniffled.

And rather than risk further wrath, she ran upstairs. Billy joined them in Sarah's room. He allowed Gill to untie Amy but Billy had to cut the wire to free Richard because the knots were so tight.

He seemed proud of his new weapon, and gave it to Richard to examine. He told them how the copper had surprised him in the alley and how he'd turned the truncheon on him. It was recounted in a light-hearted way, as if it was all one big joke.

Richard remained deadpan throughout the whole tale. Gill could tell he didn't believe a word of it. However, it served to lighten the mood. They chatted about everyday things – food they liked, places they wanted to visit, even the weather.

It was 3am. Gill had regained some of her composure. She gently suggested that they all sleep together in Sarah's room.

Richard was more upbeat. 'Excellent idea,' he said. Everyone knew why he wanted her under his protective care – including of course Billy who was exhausted anyhow and put up little resistance.

Gill went to the spare room and found three sleeping bags. They settled for the night – Amy on the bed, Gill and Richard on the floor in the middle of the room, and Billy on his stomach, his head against the door.

His trusted weapons, knife, axes and truncheon, were somewhere underneath or inside the sleeping bag.

Within seconds he was snoring. The adrenaline rush of his escape, his exhausting trek across the moors, the fights with Arthur, the stresses of keeping that house under control, the late-night drives… they'd all taken their toll. And in his fatigued state he'd left Gill untied.

Richard shuffled closer to Gill and cuddled up to her. She was trembling, totally exhausted emotionally, physically and mentally.

'Do you think he can hear us?' he whispered.

'There's no way. He's out like a light.'

'What are we going to do, Gill?'

'What do you mean?'

He was whispering so quietly even Amy couldn't hear.

'It can't go on like this. He's playing us.. like a cat with a mouse.

'No, no, no. Don't say that, don't say that. We can't take the chance of calling the police.

'That truncheon story.. a load of rubbish.'

'No… he's going in the morning. If he'd got that money tonight he'd have been off,' she murmured.

'Gill. I've been here all night. Figuring it out. We've been mugs. Please. Wise up.'

'No, you wise up. The only thing that matters, Richard, is the safety of our family.'

Richard picked his words carefully.

'As much as I hate to even contemplate it, I think he may have harmed them already.

'You saw your Dad. You said yourself he looked.. he seemed dead.'

He cuddled her tighter and lowered his voice further.

'Think about it. We can usually hear every little squeak from next door. But have you heard any movement? Sarah or Arthur going to the toilet? Any conversation?'

'Don't even think it, Richard… no, don't say it.'

'We need to somehow call the police. It's our only option.'

'No, a thousand times no..'

Amy butted in. 'Sshh you two. We don't want to wake him.'

And then she whispered the obvious.

'We could easily hit him.'

He was blocking the door of course, but Gill's hands were free. She could have got up, grabbed something heavy or sharp - Sarah's little desk, perhaps. Or, quietly untie Richard and they could team up. Knock him out cold, grab his knife, an axe, the truncheon, stab him. Surely they would win against a comatose being.

But there was no reply to Amy's suggestion. They lay in silence for what seemed an age – the turmoil of their situation overriding any hopes of going to sleep, or indeed taking up the fight.

The reality was, neither of them had the stomach for such cold-blooded acts. They simply weren't that type – the kind that could kill or maim, even though at that moment their captor was helpless.

They just couldn't do it. Maybe even Billy had sensed it too before nodding off to sleep. He didn't seem at all concerned about his safety. And he had the comfort of his trusted weapons under his body.

So, in numbed silence, they drifted off to sleep, a meaningful chance of freedom lost.

Around 4am they were awoken by a knocking on the door downstairs. It was an irregular tapping, but loud enough to be heard upstairs. Richard shook Gill. 'Did you hear that?'

KNOCK, KNOCK………… KNOCK…, KNOCK, KNOCK.

There it was again.

Billy was still comatose, but Amy was now awake too.

'Who's that?' she breathed.

All three were thrown into a silent panic, their pulses racing. They'd prayed for release, but so desperately didn't want it to be the police. It would only end in bloodshed, they were convinced of that.

KNOCK… KNOCK… KNOCK.

They felt they had no option but to wake Billy.

They rocked him from side to side, and splashed water on his face. 'Billy, wake up. There's a knock downstairs,' said Gill.

He awoke with a start and grabbed his weapons, stuffing them in his tracksuit bottoms.

'WAIT HERE,' he said, rushing from the room.

They listened on tenterhooks. He was talking. Then they heard him coming upstairs.

'It's the bloody dogs' he said. They'd been lying against the door and wagging their tails.

He'd given them a drink and they'd settled down for what was left of the night. And within a minute or so, so had Billy Hughes. And the three other people in that room.

And another chance of escape had vanished.

30

5am

The day began early for Derbyshire Police. The teleprinter in the Chesterfield Comms Room clattered out a pre-dawn weather forecast for the day – 'brighter with sunny spells.'

It was met with welcome relief all around. The heavy snow and blizzards had caused chaos with huge swathes of the county cut off. The whole of mid and North Derbyshire and to a large extent, south Derbyshire, were brought to a standstill and many officers diverted from the search operation to sort out the traffic chaos.

Nevertheless, 112 buildings, mostly isolated farms, were searched during Thursday, utilising double that number of officers. At times, visibility had been nil. Men were covered in ice and movement extremely difficult, even for four-wheeled police vehicles.

But snow ploughs and gritters had been out all night. All main roads were now passable and many of the minor roads accessible, thanks to farmers clearing the snow themselves.

CID and uniformed officers in unmarked cars had maintained overnight static observations outside Tess's home.

It was dull, monotonous work, waiting in a cold car with flasks of coffee and sarnies waiting for Hughes to make contact with her.

During the night there had been the usual calls from the public – suspicious footprints in the snow; a man hitchhiking on the moors; strangers in stranded vehicles.

But as the top brass gathered at HQ for the Friday day shift, they were interested in two developments.

An inmate from Leicester had come forward saying that Hughes had confided in him around Christmas time that he'd intended to escape and to kill his wife. An urgent message was flashed to police in Blackpool where officers had, of course, already moved Jean Hughes to a safe house.

Separately, a Detective Constable Webster of Leicestershire Police had interviewed an ex-con who claimed that he'd met Hughes in Woolworths in Leicester shortly after he'd escaped.

The man said Hughes had dyed his hair blond, and was wearing a blue and white open-necked shirt, a brown jacket with large check pattern, and blue jeans. Hughes had asked for money, and had arranged to meet him at Shirebrook Youth Club near Chesterfield on Thursday evening.

DC Webster had shown the man a photograph of Hughes and he'd confirmed it was definitely him. He was sure because he'd known him in prison. The whistle-blower had also gone to the Leicester Mercury who'd agreed to sit on the story pending police advice.

It sounded improbable, but the detective was convinced the man was telling the truth. Derbyshire Police sent one of their top detectives – DI Cooper of their Regional Crime Squad – to Leicester to interview the man. He too believed that the informant – and the information – was genuine.

Shirebrook was a small pit town in the Bolsover district of North East Derbyshire, near the border with Nottingham. On Thursday evening police had launched a plain clothes operation outside the location, and other youth clubs in the area. A dog handler and traffic car stood by at Shirebrook Police station. The informant waited outside the club as agreed, officers watching his every move. But there was no sign of Hughes, and at 9pm they called it a day. They would repeat the operation Friday evening.

Meanwhile the manhunt continued. But the weather had taken some of the impetus out of the operation. Hughes had been on the run for two days now. The trail had gone cold in more ways than one. The tip-off from jail that Hughes intended to kill his wife, reinforced the view that he'd somehow slipped the net and was indeed now back in Lancashire.

At HQ, Mitchell juggled his resources. Manpower was reduced by a third, and less than 50 buildings would be searched today – many for the second or third time. The truth was the search had stalled.

Mitchell warned Howse that if Hughes wasn't captured that day, he would have no choice but to scale down the whole thing.

31

8am

It was Gill who woke first. She could see the first signs of dawn through Sarah's thin curtains.

She stretched and gave Richard a nudge. With Billy blocking the door, they needed to wake him up before they could use the bathroom or have breakfast. Billy opened his eyes by instinct.

'Make some tea, Gill,' he said, before disappearing along the corridor to the bathroom.

She went down to the kitchen alone, glancing at the connecting door to her parents' annexe, still secured by the blood-stained flex.

Her Dad and daughter were just yards the other side of that door. But such was Billy's hold over her, she didn't give it a thought to even try to undo it.

While the saucepan boiled, she put 8 slices of toast under the grill – enough for all six of them.

Billy appeared in a tee shirt and tracksuit bottoms and moved up behind her. She felt his hands on her and he whispered how lovely she was.

The toast got her out of trouble – 'Oops, it's burning,' she said, shrugging him off.

Billy allowed Richard and Amy to go downstairs untied, certain that the chances of resistance from any of them was virtually nil.

They all sat in the kitchen enjoying tea and toast. Billy said he would take Arthur and Sarah's through, which he did.

He returned, saying how much they'd appreciated breakfast in bed, but were getting bored and that he'd promised to release them later that morning just as soon as he'd got everything together to leave.

Sarah didn't normally drink tea, but they all kept their thoughts to themselves.

Gill asked Billy that when he collected their cups could he take through some clean underwear for Sarah. He nodded.

Billy looked out the window. 'Those poor birds.' He then gathered the crumbs from the toast and went outside.

The man who'd ruthlessly murdered two humans in the house was worried about the fate of birdlife in the wintry weather.

He scrapped the snow off the bird table and left the bread.

He came back in, rubbing the goose pimples on his arms. 'Blimey, it's cold,' he said.

He then dropped another thunderbolt.

'I need you two to go shopping for me,' he said. 'Write a list. And Amy, can you boil me 13 eggs... all hard done.'

The others looked at each other wondering what this was all about. Gill fetched a notebook and he began to call out his shopping list. It was like being at work, taking dictation from the boss, although Billy was slow and deliberate, making it up as he went along.

It included a camping Gaz stove ... six tins of stew, ...two tins of tomato soup, two tins of veggie soup, a packet of four chops, two packets of glacier fruits, newspapers, and 200 John Player Special.

Then, an afterthought – 'Oh, and get a little present for Sarah. Get her something nice – an Enid Blyton book, maybe.'

'She'd like that,' said Gill.

'I nearly bloody forgot the booze,' he said, and then asked for 24 cans of light ale and a half a bottle of Bells whisky. 'Oh, and a saucepan and a tin opener.'

Amy chipped in. 'You might struggle to find those, but you can take ours if the shops are out of stock.'

He gave Gill £25 – money he'd snaffled around the house during his stay.

Gill went upstairs to get ready and Billy followed her up. He wandered into her bedroom. She was in her vest applying make-up in the mirror, the bruises and bites on her neck and upper arms visible. Billy sat on the edge of the bed watching her and she quickly reached for her polo-neck sweater.

He said nothing, just smiling at her, further tightening his psychological grip.

Outside on the drive, Richard tried to retrieve the car from the snow but the bonnet was stuck in the drift.

Gill and Billy emerged from the house. She got in the passenger seat whilst Billy went to the garage for a spade.

The engine started first time and Richard lightly touched the accelerator as Billy dug out impacted snow from under the wheel.

The Chrysler at last managed some grip and Billy pushed it from the front as it reversed onto the road. As they pulled away, Billy, wearing Richard's black ski hat with its distinctive red bobble, waved them off.

They headed towards Chesterfield. They'd travelled this route hundreds of times but never on such an extraordinary mission, thinking the lives of their loved ones were at the mercy of a madman.

Every second, they put greater distance between him and them, and for the first time in those wretched 48 hours, they were free.

They could talk openly, plan, express their feelings. There were no frantic orders in the car, mood outbursts, knife waving, sinister threats. But for the first few minutes they didn't speak at all. And then only in whispers.

Gill for one acted as if he <u>was</u> there; as if at any moment he could strike; as if everything they said he could hear.

It was Richard who broke the silence, carrying on the discussion they'd had in those early hours.

'It can't go on Gill. We're going to the police.'

The very word triggered alarm. Everything she had gone through, the fear, humiliation, degradation, everything, had been for the purpose of keeping the police AWAY!

All her life, Gill Moran had been a passive individual. She knew it herself, often saying that she wasn't very good at giving orders, but excellent at carrying them out.

In their marriage, it was Richard who ruled the roost – not in a domineering way, but gently coaxing her through difficult decisions – and she was happy with it that way.

But now, in this extreme crisis, she put her foot down. No way were they calling the police. It would be madness, she argued. They would turn up in a blaze of sirens and they'd all be dead before the police could reach the door.

'Don't be silly,' he argued back. They would use stealth, they were experts at that sort of thing. Besides, if they stopped a police car now they'd be safe.

That was too much for Gill. She accused him of putting the lives of her parents and her daughter at risk to save their own skins.

'We'd be all right Jack. I'd never be able to live with myself.'

'I keep telling you Gill. Have you even seen a light on next door! Be sensible. Face the facts.'

'He gave me his word. He would never harm her and I believe him,' she said, now in floods of tears.

Richard looked across at her. She was drained. Exhausted. Her face was white. He thought she could easily crack. And so he backed off. He reached across and held her hand.

At that moment a convoy of police cars sped past them going the other way – in the direction of the cottage.

'OH MY GOD. THEY'RE GOING TO OUR HOUSE!'

'Calm down, calm down. It's just a co-incidence,' he said, adding 'besides, … there's nothing we can do now even if they are…'

By the time they arrived at the shops, Gill had managed to compose herself. She applied make-up made and they went about their mission.

They bought the groceries at the International Shop on Chatsworth Road and bread from Henstocks Bakers next door. Further along at Johnsons, Richard purchased the camping stuff, even ordering a spare gas can, whilst Gill waited in the car.

They went into Parsons, the newsagents, together. On the counter was the Derbyshire Times, its banner headlines screaming at them. **'DANGEROUS HIJACKER STILL FREE DESPITE MOORLAND HUNT.'** The sub-heading read 'Hostage fear among police theories.'

Under a headline 'the man on the run' was a photo of Billy looking neat with short hair and sideburns. It felt eerily strange. There were pictures of police officers examining the wrecked taxi and others climbing a farm gate.

The Morans looked at each other and swallowed. Gill wanted to scream out… yes, yes, this man is at our house. We are the hostages..

They paid for the paper and Billy's cigarettes, speaking politely to the proprietor Ellen Parsons.

Gill had been pre-occupied by the headlines, and had forgotten Sarah's book. On the rack were a number of children's comics and magazines.

'Oh, I nearly forgot, have you any Enid Blyton books?'

Ellen showed her The Big Enid Blyton Book, an annual left over from Christmas. It was £2.50.

'I've got some cheaper ones if you want,' said Ellen.

'It's Okay, it's for Sarah. I'm not worried about the price.'

Ellen knew Sarah. She often came in with her granddad.

'She'll love that,' said Ellen.

After the butchers, Richard drove them to Kennings petrol station. While he filled the car, Gill read the front page of the Derbyshire Times.

There were articles on Billy's background and an interview with the injured prison officers. It was the first time she'd learned the full details of his brutal attack and she recoiled at how he stabbed the men in the car. It also said police were checking houses. The thought sent her cold.

Richard bought some oil too, paid by credit card and got back in the car. He read the paper over her shoulder. A motorist in the queue beeped his horn to move off the forecourt.

'Come on, quick. Let's go,' she said.

Travelling back, Gill felt exposed, out of her comfort zone. Extraordinary as it seemed, she wanted to be back home, under the control of the man she'd just read about. She felt safer that way. She was terrified the police would get there first. And Billy would think they'd alerted them.

'Hurry, Richard, hurry…,' she begged.

And then he realised they'd forgotten the sweets.

'Leave it, Richard, we've got to get home,' she snapped.

But he insisted, and pulled up at Kirk's sweet shop. 'If it's on the list, we're getting it,' he said.

Those few minutes waiting for him to return seemed like hours. She began to panic, ducking down in her seat so no-one could see her.

Five minutes later they arrived at Pottery Cottage. And at first it appeared her worst fears had been realised. The place was deserted. From the car she could see a note pinned to the door with a knife.

They both ran to the door. It was in fact a screwdriver rammed into the wood. The note was in her mother's handwriting. It read, 'Gone to Len and Joyce's.' It was signed Mum and Billy.

Len and Joyce were the Newmans, teachers who lived in Seconds, the end dwelling of the converted building. Billy had remembered what Amy had said when he first invaded Pottery Cottage, that she did their cleaning and had a key.

As the Morans wondered what to do, Billy and Amy emerged from the building. He was still in the bobble hat and tracksuit and was unshaven. He looked like he hadn't a care in the world. Gill breathed a sigh of relief that at last they were home and that Mum was safe.

They carried the shopping in and dumped it on the Moran's kitchen table. While Billy checked it all, the others had a cup of tea in the neighbouring Minton kitchen.

'Good job,' he said, entering the kitchen. He was carrying Sarah's Enid Blyton book. 'I'll take it through.'

Billy began untying the wire on the door. The others knew it was a waste of time requesting to go with him.

While he was gone, Amy whispered that Billy had made her go next door because he needed some money. He'd searched the Newman's home but couldn't find any. She said he'd made sure he left everything as he found it.

What she didn't know was that on exiting the building, Billy had secretly yanked the Newman's phone wire from the wall.

Noon

Gill cooked for them all – chops, potatoes and vegetables – but although Amy peeled the spuds, she said she didn't want any food and slipped silently upstairs to lay on Sarah's bed.

Billy again went through the pretence of taking Sarah and Arthur's lunch next door. What no-one could have known was that he was merely dumping meals into a bin liner next to Arthur's decomposing body.

'She loves the Enid Blyton book. I had to tell her to put it down and eat her food,' said Billy.

Amy was worn out. Her appetite had gone. Gill sensed there was something bothering her and followed her up.

Sure enough, Amy confessed that while they were out, Billy had told her that Dad had wet himself. She'd pleaded to be allowed through to help him, but Billy had refused. 'Do you think he's hurt him, Gill?'

'I'll go and ask him to let us through. But don't raise your hopes,' said Gill.

Downstairs, Billy had cracked open two beers for himself and Richard.

'Mum's just told me about Dad's incontinence. I'd like to go and see him. The poor devil must be so embarrassed,' Gill said.

Billy put down his can. 'I was hoping she wouldn't tell you, but don't worry it's all sorted.'

'What do you mean?'

'I took him to the bathroom and cleaned him up. It wasn't very nice, but there you go, it's done, and everything's now all right.'

Gill reminded Billy about a change of underwear for Sarah.

'I've gotta collect the washing-up. Get her stuff, and I'll sort her out,' he said. Gill went upstairs to the airing cupboard.

Billy took Sarah's clean knickers through. He put them in a drawer a few feet from her body.

He returned with two soiled plates, shaking his head and smiling. 'A proper little madam. She made me turn away while she changed.'

In her dark moments, thoughts that her daughter and father were dead had flitted through her mind. She couldn't avoid them. But they were too terrible to dwell on. She simply had to believe they were both alive, albeit bound and gagged, just like they'd all been.

So Billy's assurance provided a crumb of comfort for Gill. That was exactly how Sarah behaved, even in front of her.

Around 2pm they all went upstairs. Billy devoured every word of the local paper, reading sections aloud, pointing out inaccuracies, even laughing at some of the grisly details of his attack on the prison officers.

'It's only a matter of time until the cops come,' he said. 'Let's hope for all our sakes it's not in the next couple of hours, eh?,' he said.

He was troubled by his picture. It was recent. Too much like him, he said.

'Do you think you could do something about my hair, Gill?' The wig was too tight. He wanted his hair shorter for a snug fit. She spent 20 minutes or so cutting his hair, trimming the Velcro, shortening the back of the wig and styling it into shape. He liked it so much he kept it on.

Billy announced he wanted to have a bath. Could he trust them not to do anything foolish? He needn't have bothered with the warning. They'd long stopped thinking of trying to escape. They just wanted him gone.

Nevertheless, he insisted they stay in the bedroom, and for added insurance propped a broomstick against the door so they couldn't get out. They could hear him splashing about and Gill even called out to him to be careful not to get the wig wet.

Billy used her talc and his deodorant and after-shave. He then put on Richard's underpants and vest. He emerged in his own suit but wearing one of Richard's clean shirts and a tie.

They spent the afternoon chatting and drinking. There was no hostility from Billy or murmurings among the others about escape.

Around 5pm, he announced that he was short of money and asked Richard if they kept any money at his firm.

138

'Only petty cash,' said Richard. 'Everything's done by cheque these days. We're a manufacturing firm, rather than retail.'

Billy asked what time the factory closed. Richard said they worked all night but the offices closed at five. 'Right. Let's pay a little visit then,' said Billy.

He tied up Amy again but told her they wouldn't be long. He put the dogs in with her, left her some water, and switched on the transistor radio.

Richard set out along the road to Chesterfield with Gill beside him and Billy on edge, and dressed like a woman, in the back. She saw that he had brought his knife with him.

The works were ten miles away. All the way, Billy quizzed Richard about the layout, alarms, if there were security staff, what about cleaners? Questions, questions, questions, thought Gill.

The couple were about to abuse Richard's position, and felt slightly ashamed, but reasoned there was nothing they could do about it. In fact Gill silently prayed that Billy would find a load of money and flee.

Just after 6pm they arrived at Brett Plastics in Staveley. Richard pulled up at the corner and used his keys to open the main gate. He drove a few yards inside and stopped. They could see the factory lights and hear the rumble of machinery, but the nearby office block was in darkness and the car-park deserted.

Richard said he would have to go to the works to explain why he was there. Billy said okay.

Inside the factory were a dozen or so workers, all male. Richard bumped into Philip Bagshaw, the quality control officer, and explained that he'd been off sick and needed to pick up some papers to go through at the weekend. Bagshaw smiled and joked about the duties of high management.

Richard drove to the car-park, pulling up in his reserved director's space. They walked calmly to the main door.

It was cold and dark, and their breath blew tiny clouds of steam into the night air. They whispered as Richard fumbled for the right key. They were effectively doing a blag – a scenario Billy had relished scores of times in his life, but a situation alien to the Morans who felt nervous and guilty.

The alarm screamed out but Richard disappeared behind the front counter and stopped it in seconds.

Billy demanded they go to the accountant's office. Richard led the way. It was no more than a cabin with space only for a desk and chair, a four-deck Bisley filing cabinet, and a cupboard containing the company safe.

Richard handed him the key. Billy made them sit on the floor as he opened the safe. Inside were three wage packets of cash and two one-pound notes.

Billy ransacked the room, pulling out files and papers and throwing them to the ground. In less than a minute it looked like a bomb had gone off.

He rummaged through the drawers – a wad of notes here, some loose silver there. In his excitement he dropped the coins over the floor and Gill crawled around the patterned carpet to rescue them.

Billy exploded in a panic. 'I've lost my fucking knife!' Gill found it on the floor, concealed under some papers.

'Let's go,' he said.

At the door, Richard looked back at the mess and felt sick. He locked up and they hurried back to the car.

Billy took the keys and locked the factory gates behind him. He hurled the whole bunch into the night sky and leapt into the back seat.

Richard took the wheel. Billy spent the journey back tearing open wage packets and counting his loot.

'Two hundred and ten quid. Not a bad night's work,' he said. He looked at the wage slips.

'Bloody liberty. You see how much tax I've paid.'

33

7.30 pm

Back home, Billy was in a state of high excitement. He said he would be off right away. Everything about him was suddenly different. He had energy, purpose. They could tell that this time he really meant it.

He raced upstairs and untied Amy, then let the dogs out into the yard. They were his new best friends and the feeling was mutual. They were always so thrilled to see him, wagging their tails and licking his face. He responded by stroking them and having pretend fights.

The Morans daren't ask where he intended going. From his shopping list – a camping stove and the like - it would appear he was preparing to camp out. But it was the middle of winter. Formal campsites were closed for the season and he certainly didn't have a tent, even if he had thought about living rough. And that strange request for 13 boiled eggs – now cooked and cooling on the side – what were they all about?

He gathered them all for a briefing. 'Right, I'm on my way. I still don't trust you bastards, so I'm gonna have to tie you up.'

'How will we ever get free?' asked Amy.

'That's easy… Gill.'

'What do you mean?' said Gill.

'You didn't think I would leave you here, did you love? No, you're coming with me. I'll lay some distance down then stop another car.'

He said he would rob the occupants, transfer all his stuff into their car and take the people with him. 'I'll leave you with Richard's car, Gill, and you can drive back here and release everyone.'

Again, Gill started shaking. She hated the idea, but like all his actions, she had no choice but to go comply. Richard, however, didn't believe Billy for one minute. As if he would allow Gill to go free, knowing full well she'd witnessed him taking more people hostage.

She stacked his things in the kitchen while Billy packed upstairs. He'd set aside many of Richard's clothes – sweaters, shirts, underwear and the like. But now he was delving in her wardrobe selecting underwear, dresses, tops, jumpers, even evening wear and jewellery. He carried the case downstairs and put it into the boot of Richard's Chrysler.

He took the dogs up to Sarah's room. Gill could hardly bear to watch as he tied Amy and Richard's hands and feet with fresh electric cable he'd cut from the vacuum cleaner. Their arms were out in front. He couldn't pull the flex watertight, so he made three or four knots at each junction. His mood was workmanlike, almost friendly.

'This is the last time. I won't gag you in case you want a drink. And make sure you give some to the dogs,' he said.

Amy was on the bed, and Richard on the floor, leaning against the wall. Gill kissed them goodbye, trying to appear strong for her mother and husband, but she felt herself welling up and walked out before they could see her tears.

As soon as he closed the door, Richard whispered to Amy.

'We've got to break loose.'

Amy tried to wriggle out of her binds.

'Wait, wait… wait 'til he's gone,' said Richard.

Gill and Billy left the house, him with one of Richard's suits over his arm, and carrying the bag of boiled eggs.

The car started first time.

Upstairs, they waited, straining to hear the car pull away. This was it. Their moment. They had to escape and save Gill.

With every second Billy would be disappearing further and further from their lives.

Somehow they would unravel those knots, release Sarah and Arthur, run next door to the Newmans, and alert the police.

They pulled frantically at the flex around their wrists, but it was impossible to squeeze their hands through. Richard took control in his polite Irish accent. 'Amy, let's do one knot at a time.'

He shuffled across to the bed so that he could start undoing her knots with his fingers and teeth. Millimetre by millimetre the entwined flex began to loosen. They could taste the prospect of freedom.

Billy meanwhile was relaxed as they headed towards Chesterfield. He'd switched from Radio One to the Middle of The Road Radio Two.

142

Gill on the other hand couldn't stop shaking. She hadn't a clue where or when he'd hijack this other car. Maybe he would choose a motorway service station, she thought.

They drove into Chesterfield but at the traffic island at Queen's Park he realised he'd forgotten Richard's A to Z map book. 'Bollocks,' he shouted. Another mood change. 'We're gonna have to go back.'

'NO, NO, NO ... you can stop at a petrol station and buy one! There's one up here,' she pleaded.

But at the roundabout he turned full circle and headed back in the direction of Pottery Cottage five miles away.

This proved too much for Gill. Yet again, her hopes of escape had been dashed. And yet again the safety of her family became a real concern. The familiar fears returned. What if Mum and Richard have broken free and Billy walks in on them?

34

In Pottery Cottage, they were down to the last knot around Amy's wrists. Amy was shaking with excitement as Richard pulled the flex through. 'Any minute now, any minute…'

Billy pulled into the drive with his trademark screech of the brakes.

'I wanna change my clothes as well,' he said and leaned over to the back seat where he'd dumped Richard's suit. Gill thought this strange – he was already wearing his own blue pinstripe.

He told her to wait in the car, but to reverse it in so that they could make a speedier getaway once he'd changed and found the map. He got up to go and Gill noticed for the first time on that journey he'd had a knife and axe down the side of the driver's seat. He put them both in his belt and closed the car door.

Gill did as she was told, moved the car, lit a cigarette, and waited on the drive.

As he went through the front door he sensed movement upstairs. He raced up. Amy was free of her ties, but frozen to the spot in fear. Richard was crawling around on the landing, still tied up and trying desperately to break free.

With the coldness of an assassin Billy moved swiftly and silently… and reached for his knife…

On the driveway, Gill became more and more impatient. An age had passed. *Where is he? What's he doing?*

Billy appeared at the downstairs window, waving to her. She wound the window down and he called out – 'I won't be long, Gill, I'm just going in to see Dad and Sarah.'

Gill wound the window up and lit another cigarette.

Minutes later Billy was at the car door. She slid across. He turned the ignition, but the Chrysler wouldn't start.

'What have you fucking done? I bet you've had the heater on,' he said. He tried again, and again, but the battery whirred and whirred, a gradual decrescendo, until it died completely.

Gill was distraught. It was if some malevolent force was trying to stop them all from breaking loose from the clutches of this evil man.

144

She had suffered so many highs and lows in the last 56 hours, enough to send most people over the edge. She was exhausted. Mentally drained. And here again, was another massive letdown.

'We'll have to take your car,' he said.

They jumped out and moved to the garage. Only then did they fully appreciate the amount of snow that had fallen in those previous two days. It was two metres high against the garage door. Getting a car out would have been impossible.

She suggested going inside and having a cup of tea while Richard switched car batteries.

'No, we can't wait. What if someone's discovered the burglary at the factory? The police will be around in a shot. There's a tow rope in the boot. Flag a car down and we'll get a bump start.'

Gill ran into the road frantically waving at passing vehicles. But no-one would stop. Billy ordered her to go next door to the Newmans to ask for a pull out. 'Make sure you make up a good story,' he said.

'I don't want to, Billy… Don't make me go.'

'There's no other way we can get out,' he insisted.

Gill ran to the end property. She was about to knock on the door when she saw a light on in Len Newman's garage. She shouted, 'Len. You there?' He appeared, wiping his hands on a rag.

'Hello Gill.' Then he took in her demeanour - pallid, shocked, distraught. 'What's the matter, love?'

She stuttered and fumbled her words.

'It's the car.. you know Richard's car. The Chrysler. Well.. it's stuck. Er, can you give us a tow?'

Len stroked her face. 'You're drunk, Gill!'

'I haven't had a drop! My friend's in hospital and I've got to get there.. NOW!.. Please… I've got her husband with me.'

'Where's Richard?'

Gill began crying, her voice quivering. 'He's tied up! Haven't you read the papers?'

Gill herself hadn't appreciated the enormity of what she'd revealed in that moment. Her mind was befuddled. She was in such a state she didn't know what she'd said. 'I can't talk anymore. I've got to go. Just get your bloomin' car out, PLEASE!…..'

He nodded. She run back to the car.

145

Len Newman HAD read the papers. And in that snatched conversation, the awful truth had dawned. He dashed inside his home.

Billy was in the driving seat of the stricken Chrysler, facing out towards the road, so he hadn't seen her chat. She got in the passenger side and explained. They waited for Len to appear, Billy getting more and more impatient and Gill more and more desperate.

'GO AND HURRY HIM UP, FOR FUCK'S SAKE,' shouted Billy.

Gill ran back to Seconds and knocked. Len came to the door, looking haunted. 'I'm trying to catch my dog. I'll be with you as soon as I can,' he said.

She then whispered something to him, but it was all a mumble. Although he couldn't decipher her words, the message reinforced what he'd already suspected - that something was terribly wrong.

She went back to the car and told Billy about the dog.

He lit another cigarette. It seemed like an age, but they saw the lights of Len's car reversing up the drive. He passed them and backed out onto the road. They thought he was positioning the car to provide a tow. Instead there was a screech of tyres and he raced off up the road.

'The BASTARD!' said Billy. 'You've told him, haven't you!'

'No, Billy, I swear. I told him Richard was in the bath.'

Billy was fuming. But his reply was cut short.

From the shadows a figure stumbled towards them. Neither could believe what they saw.

It was Amy, blood pouting from her neck. She'd either jumped, or fallen out of an upstairs window. She was trying to speak but instead produced a moaning, gurgling sound. She held her hands out, almost begging. A warning to Gill, or a desperate plea for help? It was like a scene from a horror movie.

'OH MY GOD!' Gill screamed.

She tried to get out, but Billy pulled her back. He flashed his knife in her face and shouted, 'STAY IN THE FUCKING CAR.'

But Gill wasn't taking in anything he said at that point. She was hysterical, escaping and running around in the dark, trying to find her mother who'd disappeared from view.

Billy was panic stricken. He didn't know whether to deal with Gill – or find Amy and finish her off.

146

He was the first to find her. She was on her back, seemingly lifeless. He went to his pocket but considered her already gone. Out of sight of Gill, he dragged her further into the shadows and scooped up handfuls of snow to hide her. But he was interrupted by Gill's screams. She was in pieces.

'WHERE IS SHE? WHERE'S SHE GONE? WHAT HAVE YOU DONE TO HER?'

She looked up at the cottage. Sarah's window was open and the light on. On Dad's side of the house... darkness.

WHAT'S HE DONE TO THE OTHERS?

She tried to find Amy, but bumped into Billy coming the other way. He grabbed her by the arm and pulled her away. 'COME ON,' he ordered.

She was screaming at him. 'WHAT HAVE YOU DONE WITH MUM?, WHAT HAVE YOU DONE WITH MUM?'

He pulled her along the road, forcing her to run. Each time a car came along he threw her into the snowy ditch, pressing down on her head until the lights passed. He tried to reassure her.

'She cut herself jumping out. I've put her in the kitchen, she's okay,' he said. But Gill didn't believe a word.

'YOU'VE HARMED HER. I KNOW YOU HAVE.'

They reached the Highwayman Inn. The car-park was busy. He wondered what to do. Stealing a car was too risky.

Billy dragged her on. At the first house, he made her climb a wall into the garden. They walked through, but there was no sign of a car and it looked as if no-one was in. On they went. She was bitterly cold and soaked to the skin. Ice and snow were in her wellies and coat pockets. Billy spotted two cottages.

'Who lives there?' he said.

Gill happened to know. The first was occupied by an elderly couple, so she told him about the second property.

'It's Ron Frost. He's a mechanic. He's got a pick-up.'

'Just the man,' said Billy, 'just the fucking man.'

They went to the back door and knocked. Billy held her tight. He could feel her trembling through her coat.

'Who is it?' a voice queried from inside.

'Mag, it's Gill from down the road.'

147

Maggie Frost opened the door. It took her a few moments to respond to the sight on her doorstep - her neighbour in wellies and a skirt, white sweater and a green coat splattered with mud. She was bedraggled and shivering. A man in a sopping wet wig and a summer suit had his arm around her.

'Blimey, you're soaked. Come inside, quick.'

Ron Frost came down the stairs.

'My word, look at you! What's happened?'

Billy replied in a quiet, friendly and rational tone. They were hoping to visit his wife in hospital but were having a bit of trouble with the car. 'We're stuck on Gill's drive. I think it's the solenoid, but I'd appreciate a tow to bump start it.'

While Billy spoke, Gill stared intently at Maggie. Their eyes met. And Gill mouthed… 'SAVE ME!'

Maggie smiled nervously. A fraction of a second. Had she got the message? Gill's heart raced. She thought of the knife in Billy's outside pocket. What if Mag gave it away? All it would take is a stupid slip of the tongue, or one foolish act.

'The truck's in the garage, I'll get my coat,' said Ron.

The three of them walked to the garage. Then Maggie called her husband back, leaving Billy and Gill waiting in the cold. He returned a few moments later looking stern and businesslike.

Billy pushed Gill into the front seat and jumped in beside her. It gave Gill a split second to turn to Ron. 'Help me, Ron,' she mouthed. He nodded. She clung to his arm as they pulled away - squeezed between a killer and her saviour. For that moment at least she felt safe.

Derbyshire Police Log, Friday January 14th 1977.

8.08pm message … I am at Smart's Farm, Eastmoor. I have been told that the escaped prisoner has a family at ransom up here. I will wait at Smart's Farm for your officers.'

From: Mr Newman, Pottery Cottages.
Received by: Comms Room, Chesterfield West.
Means: Telephone.

35

Len Newham had been plunged into a crisis. Gill pleading with him to help, seeing the escaped prisoner on her drive, hearing the screams. AND SOMEONE HAD CUT HIS PHONE.

Len and his wife had frantically debated what to do. Should he escape via the back garden, run up the road to the pub? No, he would go along with Gill's request for a tow. But at the last second he'd changed his mind. Once on the road he decided to make a dash for a phone.

He knew that every second exposed the Moran family to escalating degrees of risk. He needed to call the police, quickly, either from a call box, or from someone's home. He saw a farm with its lights on and screeched to a halt.

Charlie Smart and his wife were watching TV with a friend when there was a thunderous knocking on the back door. When he opened it he found Len in a frenzy.

'Phone.. phone. I must use your phone,' he begged.

His 999 call, just after 8pm, sent Derbyshire Police into overdrive. 'Family at ransom,' was the message they'd expected but had feared.

Most of the senior officers had gone off duty. They were scrambled from home and instructed to attend Chesterfield sub-division HQ for a briefing.

The team staking out a youth club at Shirebrook, in case Hughes had turned up to meet the prison informant, were diverted to Eastmoor.

The operator told Len to wait at the farmhouse for the police to arrive. He put the phone down and explained to the Smarts what had happened.

Smart went to his safe, got out his shotgun and began to load. His wife locked all the windows. They rang neighbours, urging them to assemble at his house – and to bring their firearms.

Three minutes after his 999 call, Len Newman received a call back from Detective Inspector Hulme who wanted him to go over his story again. He was on his way, he said. In the meantime could Len draw a sketch plan of the cottage layout and note down details of the occupants?

At 8.27pm – nearly half an hour after the first call- Charlie Smart phoned 999 again, complaining bitterly about the lack of police action. He was still waiting for someone to arrive.

In fact, it had been decided to set up an emergency control room in the Highwayman Inn, near the farm, and just up the road from the cottage.

A convoy of police cars and tracker dogs assembled in the car-park. To the amazement of regulars enjoying the start of the weekend, police took over the snug bar and commandeered access to the phones.

Divisional Commander Chief Supt Unwin, who had been on leave, arrived to control the operation. After consulting with Mitchell at Force HQ, the order went out that no-one was to approach Pottery Cottage until further notice.

36

It took two minutes for Ron Frost to drive his pick-up truck to Pottery Cottage. There, stranded on the drive, was Richard Moran's bronze Chrysler. And buried in the darkness, unseen to Ron, was the body of Amy Minton.

Ron parked his vehicle on the road and began to connect the tow rope. Billy ordered Gill to sit in the passenger seat while he helped. Billy got in beside her and waited for Ron to pull away. The tow snapped. Billy got out in a huff.

'Leave it to me,' Ron said, and Billy got back in the car.

Ron was playing for time. Had Maggie got through to 999?

He tied the rope again. Deliberately loose. And as he pulled away, it came off again. Ron was playing a high-risk game. The man had a blood-stained boning knife hidden in his pocket. And he was fast losing patience. For a third time, Ron attached the tow rope. This time, it held. They pulled away - west, towards Baslow.

But the Chrysler wasn't running under its own steam. Billy repeatedly slipped the car into gear and lifted the clutch with no sign of the engine starting. Ron wondered what the hell was going on in the car behind. Billy realised he hadn't switched the ignition on.

After more attempts, the engine burst into life. He revved repeatedly then gave Ron a couple of hoots. Ron stopped and got out. They watched him through the windscreen take an age to unhook the tow rope.

'He must be the slowest fucking mechanic in history,' said Billy. He tooted the horn again. Ron jumped out of his skin. He approached the driver's window and handed over the rope. Billy threw it in the back.

'Thanks, mate. Let me give you a drink,' Hughes said, reaching into his trouser pocket.

'No, that's fine. Only happy to help,' said Ron.

Gill watched forlorn and frightened as Ron walked back to his vehicle. She was helpless and alone. Again.

Billy calmly set off west on the A619, anxious to put some distance down, but keeping within the speed limit to avoid police speeding stops.

'What's the best way to the M6?' he asked her.

Gill knew the area well. He could go via Macclesfield, but that was over the tops, and would be icy. Or he could go to Chapel-en-le-Frith which was a better route. He smiled at her and said, almost sweetly, 'Oh, we'll go your way, then.'

Gill put the heater on full blast. Light music played and they chain-smoked. He thrust the whisky bottle into her hands. 'It'll do your nerves good,' he said. She thanked him and drank a mouthful. She went along with everything he suggested, knowing for certain he had no compunction about killing her.

Her feet were numb, so she pulled her wellies off, emptying the melted snow out the window. She held the steering wheel while Billy took his Cuban heels and socks off. She directed the heat onto their feet and massaged her toes.

   ***

Ron Frost had raced back, trying to memorise the registration of the car he'd just towed. Frustratingly, he didn't have anything to write with, so he repeated the numbers and letters out loud hoping they would stick. 'Bronze K..W..G..K…W…G.'

The Highwayman Inn car-park was awash with police vehicles. He screeched to a halt and grabbed the first copper he saw. But in his excitement he got the make wrong, saying it was a Hillman, rather than a Chrysler.

'It's him! The Hughes fella. He's taken Mrs Moran. It's a Hillman, bronze Hillman. K Reg.. yeah, definitely K reg.' He couldn't remember the rest.

Three detectives from the Regional Crime Squad – DI Geoff Cooper, DS Brian Slack and DC Bob Meek jumped into their Morris Marina squad car. Another cop, TDC Chris McCarthy, joined them. They drove at speed, but with no siren or blue light.

On the police airwaves, an alert went out to look out for a K - Registered bronze Hillman being driven by a man and a woman. It was broadcast with a warning that the man was a violent escaped prisoner and could be armed.

Billy and Gill's route took them through the heart of the Peak District, bypassing several picture-postcard tourist destinations, including Eyam, the famous 'bubonic plague' village.

It had taken the detectives ten minutes or so to spot a bronze car - near the Three Stags Inn at Wardlow Mires. And there it was, straight ahead. But it wasn't a Hillman and it was difficult from the rear to get a good look at the passengers.

Billy's eyes were glued to his rear mirror. He became troubled.

'There's a police car behind,' he said, drawing on his cigarette.

Gill turned around. She could see the lights of a car but it didn't look like a police vehicle.

'You're imagining things,' she said.

But he was a lifelong crook. He could sniff the police a mile off.

Billy put his foot down – not a dramatic acceleration, but gradually going faster, his eyes fixed to the headlights of the car in the rear mirror. Forty, fifty, sixty, miles an hour.. but the Marina stayed right behind.

'FUCKING BASTARDS,' shouted Billy at no-one.

They decided to overtake, to determine one way or another the identity of the occupants. They chose Tideswell Four Lane Ends to make his move, where there was good street lighting.

Billy stayed cool as the Marina passed. His head was still, seemingly concentrating on the road ahead, but his eyes were focussed on his wing mirror. Four blokes. *FUCKING COPS.*

The Marina accelerated off. For a second or too, Billy thought he might have been mistaken.

But after taking a bend, there it was, parked up with its hazard lights flashing. A man was in the road waving them down.

'Fuck it,' said Billy. He drove straight at him at 50 mph. Meek dived for cover, a split-second away from almost certain death. He scrambled back into the squad car. The chase was on.

Billy was now on a total high.. swearing back at the coppers and reaching speeds of 80 miles an hour. Gill slumped down in fear and panic and reached for her seat belt - 'SLOW DOWN,' she screamed.

The detectives radioed HQ with details of the car, saying they were virtually certain it was Hughes and a woman and the car was a Chrysler. But alas, further frustration. The A623 climbed deep into the Peak Forest. The reception broke up mid call, before they could radio their exact position. They weren't sure how much of their message had got through.

At the first phonebox, at Sparrowpit, they jettisoned Meek, so he could telephone the details of the car and precisely where they were. The Marina roared off in pursuit.

The Derbyshire Police Control Room was on the top floor to ensure the best radio signal possible.

Inspector John Keen was in charge that night. He had a reputation as a safe pair of hands, someone who remained calm and composed under pressure. He became the lynchpin of a dramatic fast-moving operation involving three forces - Derbyshire, Greater Manchester and Cheshire.

They hatched a plan to intercept Hughes at the junction with the A6 at Barmoor Clough, parking two cars across the road, with their blue lights flashing and rather hopefully putting down a 'POLICE STOP' sign.

At the road block, Billy braked dramatically and swerved into the offside carriageway, just missing the 'Keep Left' bollards. The police scrambled like the 24-hour Le Mans race.

Hughes was buzzing, driving more and more recklessly, at speeds of 100 miles an hour. Then, at a slight right-hand bend, the police forced him into a wall.

Cooper rushed towards the stricken car. Inside, Billy and Gill were shaken, but had escaped injury. Billy was first to react. He tried to smash the windscreen with the handle of his axe.

Cooper stopped in his tracks a few feet from the passenger door. Hughes had the woman pinned down and was holding a knife at her throat.

'FUCKING BACK OFF OR SHE GETS THIS,' he screamed.

'Just let the lady go,' said Cooper.

Gill was hysterical, screaming and shouting.

'He means it… PLEASE… I beg you. Do as he says.'

The others arrived at the car, but Cooper halted them with his arm. They had no choice but to retreat. And they knew a police Range Rover was nearby.

Cooper thought he'd try again, and approached the Chrysler alone.

Before he could even speak, Hughes repeated his threat to slash Gill's throat. He demanded another car - and a clear run.

154

Cooper took stock. Hughes held all the cards. They had little assistance. And at least they now had the Range Rover as backup.

'Okay, okay, okay... Don't do anything daft, son. You can take our car.'

He called for the keys, but Hughes intervened.

'Pull it up here and leave them in the ignition,' he said. 'And if you try anything, she's dead...'

Slack rolled the Squad Car up.

'Now. BACK OFF. RIGHT BACK.. All of ya, behind that Range Rover.'

The detectives retreated. They watched helplessly as Hughes, in bare feet, pushed the woman out of the passenger seat and dragged her towards their squad car, the axe poised over her head.

Such was Gill's state, she had taken none of the negotiations in. She had no idea it was a police car. She could hear crackling from the radio but thought it was the engine about to catch fire.

She screamed at Billy. 'We can't get into this.. it's going to blow up. It's been in a bump.'

'No it hasn't,' said Billy. 'It's a fucking police car.'

Only then, it hit home. She could see a couple of uniforms in a Range Rover. She felt relieved, not just at their presence, but that she was still alive. She felt like running to them, screaming to the world that she didn't want to get in that car. But she was forced to. And he had taken with him the knife and the axe. He pushed her into the passenger seat and sped off. The chase was on again.

For 45 minutes, they followed Hughes, up hills, down dales, around in circles, then along the A6 through Chapel-en-le-Frith, Whaley Bridge, Furnace Vale to Newtown at speeds up to 90 mph.

The convoy crossed in and out of Cheshire and Lancashire and Derbyshire with reinforcements arriving all the time. A trail of flashing blue lights and wailing sirens filled the night sky.

Attempts to stop him failed miserably. Once he simply crashed through a police dog van, taking half the bodywork with him. He did the same at Horwich End, where he left the A6 and joined the A5002 towards Macclesfield.

Gill was in a mental meltdown. The world – her life - flashed by, blue signs for Stockport and Manchester, the faces of mum, dad, husband and daughter.

She didn't know where they were heading – and neither did he. All she could do was to close her eyes. And pray. Silently.

37

8.45pm

Confirmation that the man on the run was almost certainly William Thomas Hughes, meant it was safe to search Pottery Cottage.

Several officers walked down from the Highwayman. They spotted a mound of fresh snow at the rear of the drive. Detective Sergeant Bill Miller approached. He could just make out a trail of speckled blood leading to what was obviously a body partially covered with snow.

He was anxious not to disturb any evidence, but it was essential to establish if this person was dead or alive. He felt for a pulse. Nothing. He carefully shifted the snow so he could see the face. It was a woman, dark hair, elderly, maybe in her late sixties or early seventies.

He radioed into control and gave Keen the details.

Miller left his colleagues to guard the body while he looked inside. He tried the front door but it was locked. He walked around the back. The inside lights were on, an upstairs window was open, and he could hear radio music from inside.

Miller was a big, muscular man, in his late thirties. He put his shoulder to the rear door and entered. The two dogs came at him wagging their tails. He let them out in the yard.

He stood in the doorway of the kitchen and studied the scene – a round table with chairs, sink, cooker, washing machine, cupboards, and then, over by the door, a pile of electric flex and half a dozen or so 13-amp plugs with their cables still attached.

He moved through to the other kitchen. Everything was spotless. All the cutlery and crockery had been put away. It was as if the cleaners had just been. A sliding glass door leading through to the living room, was tied shut with flex.

He went through the hall into the lounge. Again, everything was immaculately tidy. He walked through to the dining area – and almost stumbled over a body.

157

It was an old man. In an easy chair, hidden in the alcove, bound and gagged with flex. A false leg was on the floor. A teddy bear had been carefully balanced on his chest.

Miller could tell instantly the man was dead, and had probably been so for two or three days. He switched his radio on. 'Body of elderly man in downstairs lounge with severe number of stab wounds,' he told Keen.

The sergeant was careful not to touch anything. But his duty was to search the building for signs of life.

He gingerly climbed the stairs. On the upstairs landing, was the body of a middle-aged man, partially tied to a broken chair, with blood still dripping onto the floor. There were two blood-stained knives beside him and two strands of electric flex.

He took his pulse. Again, nothing. For the third time in as many minutes, he reported into control what he'd discovered. 'Male, aged about 40, with multiple knife wounds to the chest and throat.'

The master bedroom was empty. He looked at the gallery of family photos – the old man and the woman, the middle-aged man with his wife whom he knew had been taken hostage in the car. But where was the little girl in the picture?

He checked her bedroom. Other bits of chair were scattered on the floor and a trail of blood led to the open window where the woman had crashed through. On the floor were loose bindings as if someone had escaped.

He stepped across and looked out the window onto the yard. On the patio was a shattered plant pot as if someone, the old lady, he deduced, had fallen on it.

Miller checked the upstairs spare room. Nothing of significance. But the secured kitchen door downstairs was bugging him and he went back down.

The whole property was now a crime scene and he had to be careful where he trod and what he touched. But the girl might still be alive through that door.

Using a kitchen towel, he undid the flex on the connecting door then wandered through into the living room. Everything seemed in order.

He climbed the stairs and entered the first bedroom. He pinched his nose at the smell. On the floor at the bottom of the bed was a little girl in school uniform, trussed with a clothes line and gagged. She'd been stabbed through the heart and throat.

The sergeant winced. Nearby was her elephant comforter, an Enid Blyton manual, and a plastic bin liner smelling of rotting food. As a father himself he wanted to pick her things up and tidy them around her body. Instead, he reached for his radio again.

Miller went outside for some fresh air. He told the others what he'd found and disappeared to the front of the house to regain his composure taking deep breaths of the cold winter air.

Soon the business of murder would begin and the experts arrive – the senior officers, scenes of crime people, forensics, pathologist, police photographers, preservers of the scene, morticians.

He felt physically sick. He lit up and paced up and down in the snow, looking up at the stars and wondering. About life; motive; luck (he lived nearby and had two kids of his own); cruelty; evil; About how he hated – and loved – his job in almost equal measure.

38

9pm

Bakewell Police Station

Bakewell was a small market town known more widely for its Pudding than for any crime. The police station was a small Victorian building on the edge of Market Place.

The two duty patrol officers were on their way back from Buxton where they'd escorted two suspects for overnight confinement ready for court the following day.

The station was having heating issues and in the cramped CID office on the first floor, Detective Constable Johnny Burton was holding the fort wrapped in his winter coat. He was wondering about a crafty pint on the way home when the female voice from control echoed across the empty room.

It was probably the most dramatic – and sombre – news ever relayed by Derbyshire Police. Four bodies found in a house, including a girl, and the suspect, William Thomas Hughes, was on the run having taken a female hostage.

Burton rang his boss immediately – Chief Inspector Howse, the man in charge of the hunt for Hughes in the Buxton area, who lived in a police house nearby.

Howse grabbed his coat. Within no time, Burton, Howse and Sergeant Eric Cross joined the chase in a police Panda car.

They radioed in – 'We're heading north and will maintain radio silence until we catch up.'

They were a good 45 minutes behind, but from updates on the force radio, Hughes appeared to be going around in circles, and the Buxton trio had the advantage of knowing the area intimately, including short cuts over the tops.

At the same time, Mitchell in HQ ordered that the police armoury at Buxton be opened. He gave the order for firearms and CS Gas to be used if necessary.

Two newly-trained firearms officers – Detective Sergeant Frank Pell and Detective Constable Alan Nicholls - were issued with Smith and Wesson .38 calibre double-action revolvers – particularly designed for close quarters work - and a stock of bullets.

They gave chase, but, like Howse and his men, were many miles from the convoy.

Billy drove fast through the dark and icy country roads. Behind him was a line of police cars, all feeding back locations.

'YOU'LL GET US BOTH KILLED,' Gill yelled.

'Get on the radio. Tell 'em to back off.'

Gill fumbled for the receiver, but she hadn't a clue how to operate it.

'Hello.. hello… can anyone hear us? Please back off. I repeat, please back off,' she yelled. Billy snatched it out of her hand.

'Back off you bastards, or she's dead meat. You hear?' he bellowed. There was no reply – except a monotone of cackle. Billy smashed the handset against the dashboard.

Every officer with access to a police radio could monitor the progress of the chase.

They learned in disbelief how Hughes had killed four of the Pottery Cottage occupants; how a dozen cars were hot on his tail; how Mitchell had instructed officers at roadblocks to arm themselves by commandeering farmers' shotguns; how the police armoury at Buxton had been opened and weapons issued; how trained marksmen were on their way.

Also listening with incredulity was a young PC on duty in the Cheshire village of Rainow. He was alone in his panda in a pub car-park keeping an eye on the usual Friday night pub scene.

The radio cackled …. 'we're on the A5002 heading towards Rainow…'

The officer's ears almost popped. His heart missed a beat. They were heading his way!

He dashed from the car, desperate for inspiration. At that moment, a single-decker bus pulled up, disgorging passengers at the pub. He ran to the driver. 'I'm commandeering this bus.'

'I'm not sure…' said the driver, but the officer was insistent and full of urgency.

The PC ordered everyone off, and directed the driver to park side-on, thus blocking the road. Within a minute or so the convoy of headlights and sirens came speeding down the hill into the village.

Hughes wasn't immediately sure what it was across the road in front of him. He flashed his lights. Full beam.

'IT'S A BUS!!!' cried Gill.

Hughes braced himself to crash through it, but at the last second realised this was futile and slammed on the brakes. His car spun out of control, careered into a snowy ditch, and crashed head-on into a garden wall.

Behind, a dozen or so police cars screeched to a halt. Cops sprang out from every car wondering what to do. They could hear screams and shouts – the plaintive cries of a hysterical woman, the frenzied threats of the man holding her.

Gill Moran wasn't sure if she was hurt or not. All she could hear was Billy shouting 'GET AWAY, YOU BASTARDS.'

There was a stand-off. Who was in charge? More cars arrived.

Then, from the back of the pack of officers, a tall figure emerged. 'I'm a Chief Inspector. Anyone here above that rank?'

There was no reply.

39

10.15pm

Rainow, Cheshire

There was a running gag amongst rank and file coppers that the way to reach the top was to never make a decision. The brass always delegated, passed the buck. They grabbed the glory if an operation was a success but shifted the blame when it went tits up.

But there comes a point in every career when a man must step forward and do his duty. And this, in his 20th year as a police officer, was Chief Inspector Peter Howse's date with destiny.

Born in Glossop, Derbyshire in 1938, he'd attended the local grammar school and after National Service in Iraq, involved in intelligence and signals, he thought he'd quite like to become a teacher.

But he missed the boat for college, and instead found himself signing up to be a young bobby in Derby.

Now aged 40, he had control of his own patch. He'd had stints in uniform, vice and drugs, and CID. As an inspector, he'd been selected to spend time in America to study policing there.

But nothing in his career, no amount of training or tuition, could have prepared him for this moment – negotiating on a snowy rural road, face to face with an axe-wielding crazed murderer threatening to kill a hostage.

There was only one priority. He was certain of that. And that was to save the woman. At all costs. Arresting the fugitive was necessary, but secondary. But Howse was vulnerable. No weapon, no back-up - an unarmed cop with simply his wits to prevent another bloodbath.

The disabled green Morris was twenty yards away, in front of the barricade bus. It was marooned at an angle, its engine contracting and dead.

Howse advanced in trepidation, straddling the white line in the middle of the road, leaving the blue lights and cackling radios behind him. He looked more like a rambler than a police officer – there'd been no time to put his uniform on, only to grab his walking jacket. His boots crunched on the shattered glass.

In those few seconds he weighed up the geography. The car was virtually in the garden of a house. It was going nowhere. There were six feet snowdrifts on the side of the road. There was no traffic. He figured that beyond the bus, his Cheshire colleagues must have closed the road.

It was dark, but the headlights from the police convoy offered enough light for Howse to see inside the car.

Hughes was in the front passenger seat looking back at him, his back to the dashboard He was forcing Gill's neck back over the seat, holding an axe over her head.

'COME NEAR ME AND SHE FUCKING GETS IT. STAY BACK. GET THE FUCK BACK.'

She was shaking so much that Hughes jumped up and down on her to get her to remain still. He held the axe inches from her face.

Instinctively some of Howse's colleagues crept in the shadows in support, but they were clumsy and Hughes spotted them.

'BACK OFF. I CAN FUCKING SEE YOU!!'

Howse theatrically ordered everyone back, shouting and gesticulating with both arms. He had no game plan. He could only act on instinct. But the most obvious initial strategy was to try to calm Hughes down.

The rear offside passenger side window had smashed in the collision and Howse had a line of sight with Hughes. He stopped at the rear door and bent down on his haunches, hands in the air, like in a Western. It was as if he was a gunslinger and Hughes the sheriff.

Hughes had been his obsession for the last three days. He'd never met him, only seen pictures in the rogue's gallery and press. Now he could see the contours of his face and the whites of his eyes. One seemed blue, the other brown, but he wasn't certain.

'Calm down, son. There's only me here now. Just you and me. It's been a bit of a night for both of us. We both need a clear head here.'

'BACK, BACK... I'M WARNING YA... I'VE A KNIFE IN HER SIDE AS WELL.'

'HE HAS, HE HAS,' screamed Gill.

She was naturally petrified. Hughes was squeezing her neck so tightly, she could hardly breathe. 'PLEASE BILLY, NO... DON'T

164

KILL ME, BILLY.' And then she begged to Howse, 'PLEASE DO AS HE SAYS.'

Howse latched on to her use of Hughes' Christian name. He was determined to talk quietly and evenly, no shouting, the tone of a teacher he'd always wanted to be.

'Okay, Billy. Let's just talk. There's no need to harm her.. calm down.'

'YOU'RE TOO CLOSE. FUCKING GET BACK. YOU HEAR?'

Howse retreated a yard. He was still within six feet of the rear door, and able to see inside.

'All right Billy. I won't try anything. First, put the axe down. We can't talk with that hanging over her head. You've nothing to bother about. I couldn't get at you even if I wanted to. Everyone's too far away.'

Billy was wired.. looking in every direction, fearing he was about to be rushed.

Howse pressed on – 'Come on Billy, you don't want to harm her, she's been all right with you. You're a family man yourself.. you've got a wife and kid of your own.'

'I'm not fucking bothered. No fucker cares about me now. I'll take every fucker with me if I have to.'

Gill pleaded, 'He doesn't mean it. He thinks a lot of his daughter. He told me so.. it's true isn't it, Billy?'

'Come on Billy, you wouldn't like your girl to be in this position. Think about it. Gill's looked after you for three days and done everything you asked. You must think a lot of her, after all she's done for you. Just be fair, that's all I'm asking. Give her a chance. You don't want to harm her. It'll just make your situation worse.'

Hughes lowered the axe down to his lap – a minor victory for Howse. But she could still feel the knife in her side.

Howse tapped into Billy's ego. 'Come on, Billy. This isn't your scene. This is all kid's stuff, well below your league. You can see she's terrified. I know your background. You're a hard man.'

Unfortunately Gill wasn't on the same wavelength. 'He's not a hard man, he's not. He won't hurt anyone if you keep your word with him. You'll keep your word, won't you Billy?'

165

Howse tried to rescue his tactic – 'All right, he'll keep his word, but he's still a hard man. He shouldn't need a woman hostage with his reputation.'

'Who the fuck are you anyway?,' said Hughes.

'I'm Chief Inspector Peter Howse, Derbyshire Police man and boy. You can call me what you like, but I'm OK with Pete. Or Howsey, as the lads in the station like to say.'

The rank seemed to impress Billy. 'Fucking hell! You look more like a farmer than a chief inspector.'

'Well, they dragged me out halfway through Gunsmoke. Come on, Billy. I'm giving you a way out here. Give me the axe and we can talk.'

'Fuck off.'

Billy then made his first demand. He wanted a police car with a full tank of petrol – one with a flashing blue light and a police radio that worked.

'I can get you those, Billy. But I want the woman first. It's only fair. Give me your word and you can have the car.'

Gill had calmed to a degree – 'Billy, please, give him your word. He's a reasonable man, he wouldn't lie to you.'

'GET ME THE FUCKING CAR! UP HERE. NOW!!!!'

Another change of tack was needed. Howse upped the ante, on tone and language.

'Fucking hell, Billy what are you talking about! You know I can't let you take her. Do you think we're fucking daft? You've had a good run, let her go. Give me the axe and the knife and we'll talk about it.'

Howse looked at his watch – coming up to 10.30.

'It's nearly closing time. There's a pub down the road. Come on, I'll buy you a pint and we can talk in the warm. I'm fucking freezing out here.'

'I've told you.. bring up the car,' Billy insisted.

'How far do you think you'll get? At least you know where you stand with me. All they can do is to send you to prison for a spell and one day you'll be out... a free man.'

'You obviously don't know me. There's no fucking way I'm ever going in there again. If I do, I'll have taken all you bastards with me.'

'Well good luck with that mate, but let her go first. Even hard men see sense.'

'What about guns… who's got 'em?'

Howse stood up and held out his arms.

'You know better than that, Billy. We don't carry guns. If anyone had one it would be me, right?'

Howse sensed a breakthrough.

'Just look me in the eye and give me your word about Gill here.'

Billy thought for a second or two and offered an unconvincing 'all right.'

And then, as in this whole remarkable Pottery Cottage saga, there was another unexpected twist of fate. In the confusion of the ambush, no-one had informed the householder about what was happening the other side of his garden wall. He ventured into the yard to see what all the fuss was about, triggering the security light in his garden.

It was like someone turning up the gas under a simmering pan of water. Billy went into boiling point, grabbing the axe again, and holding it over Gill's head. She screamed for mercy.

'YOU'RE FUCKING TRICKING ME, YOU BASTARD.'

'Billy, listen. That light is in that bloke's house. It's nothing to do with me.'

'I want every fucking light turned off. Tell your men to turn their headlights off.'

The rise in tension caused two officers to crouch down and creep towards the car. Again Billy saw them. Howse again had to tell them to back off. Howse was back to square one. Worse, he sensed that Billy was reaching the end of his tether and that Gill was in serious jeopardy.

'Okay, okay.. all right, calm down Billy. Here's what I'm going to do. I'm going back there to arrange for a car. It'll take a minute or so. You have my word that you can have the car and we'll discuss what to do about Gill. Just don't do anything daft, okay Billy? Give me your word, Billy.'

'All right, but hurry. And I want some fags as well.'

Howse, deflated and angry, gingerly backed off and headed back to the waiting pack.

'That fucking light..'

'You're doing great, guv,' said Cross.

The team had been giving HQ a running commentary.

'There's a psychiatrist on the way to help in the negotiations guv.'

'For Hughes or for me?' said Howse.

Howse ordered a Panda car be made ready for Hughes.

As he pondered his next move, there was a welcome tap on his back. Pell and Nicholls, the firearms team, had finally arrived with their revolvers.

40

10.45pm

Hughes wondered what the fuck was going on back there. He could see movement in the shadows, policemen in huddles, with that Howse bloke at the centre of things.

He didn't trust any of the bastards. They were probably fiddling with the car; emptying it of petrol, doing something to the engine so that it would cut out after a short time.

He wondered whether Gill was any use to him now. She was becoming a liability. He wasn't bothered if she lived or died. She was simply a negotiating tool.

He looked at Gill 'While I'm here threatening you, they're likely to shoot me to save you. But if I kill you, they'll just overpower me and arrest me. Weird shit, eh?'

Gill couldn't take anything in. She hadn't realised he was a cop until he'd said his name. She thought he was just some random bloke, an indication as to the state of her mind. How she yearned for the protection of that friendly voice to return. She wanted to get out and put her arms around him..

She asked Billy softly, 'When the car comes, you going to let me go, Billy?'

He was deep in thought.

'Is that right, Billy?'

'No… you're coming with me to the motorway. I'll drop you off, you'll be all right.'

Now, perhaps for the first time in that whole nightmare she was beyond believing anything he said. He still had the axe near her face. She was still shaking. He still had her by the throat.

Billy noticed the outline of Howse walking towards them.

'Where's the fucking car?'

'It's coming… I've brought you these..'

It was two cigarettes. Gill lit one for Billy.

'I'll call the car up,' said Howse.

Howse waved to the back. Cross pulled up in the Panda and stopped just behind the Morris. The positioning was precise and deliberate. It would be perfect cover. He then returned to the pack, leaving the keys in the ignition. But that car was going nowhere.

Howse held the driver's door open.

'There you go, Billy, yours for the taking. But you've got to take me instead of Gill. Let her go.'

'FUCK OFF, I'M NOT A MUG, YOU'LL JUMP ME,' said Billy.

Gill became hysterical again.

'OH PLEASE, PLEASE BILLY. LET ME GO.'

Then he made a new demand – more fags and a pair of size 8 shoes.

'I'll see what I can do,' said Howse. He walked back to the convoy.

'Right, listen up. Anyone got size eight shoes?' The question was greeted with stony silence.

One of the officers was Chris McCarthy, who'd been in the chasing pack – and who'd coincidentally been on duty the night Hughes raped the woman in the park the previous summer.

Howse looked down at McCarthy's footwear – smart black Italian shoes purchased from Ravel. 'What size are they?' 'Er, size eight, guv.'

'C'mon. Hand them over.' Howse took them back to the car for Hughes, leaving McCarthy standing in his socks in the frozen snow.

Howse this time deliberately went to the front of the car to change Billy's eyeline away from the rear.

'WHAT YOU DOING? MOVE BACK!, MOVE BACK YOU BASTARD,' screamed Billy.

Howse did so, marginally, and asked if he could put the shoes and cigarettes on the back seat. Billy agreed and Howse put his hands through the broken window. He then adopted his previous crouching position, but now only a yard away.

Having just demanded that all surrounding lights be turned off, Hughes now wanted floodlights, so that he could see what was happening in the shadows.

Howse wondered if Hughes had somehow got a whiff of the conversation he'd just had with the firearms officers who preferred the cover of darkness. He had no choice but to arrange for the lights of bus to be turned on full beam.

'Now back away while I put the shoes on,' Billy demanded.

It was the distraction that the armed officers needed. Whilst Billy bent down to sort his footwear, Pell and Nicholls moved up slowly in a crouching position, using the Panda as cover. They were out of sight, but close enough to hear and see what was going on inside.

'Right, Billy, I've kept my side of the bargain. The car's there, its engine running. Let her go and we'll ride off into the sunset together, you and me,' said Howse.

No one will ever know what triggered Hughes' next move. But the stand-off was about to end. He flew into a rage, shouting to Gill, 'Your time is up.'

He raised the axe above her head. Gill cowered. She was a second away from certain death.

But Howse dived through the rear window to block the axe, his legs still dangling outside.

A shot rang out. BANG!

Hughes frantically tried to bring the weapon down on Gill, but the confined space – and Howes' intervention – diverted the axe, just brushing her face.

Billy was fighting mad and tried to hit her with it again, but Howse manoeuvred his body between Hughes and Gill, protecting her head with one arm, while trying to wrestle the axe from Hughes' grip with the other. As they grappled, two more shots were fired.

BANG! BANG!

Followed by a fourth.

BANG!

All this is a fraction of a second.

The first shot was delivered by Pell from the back of the car through the window. It entered Hughes' head but it failed to penetrate his skull.

And rather than incapacitate him, it spurned him on, shouting 'bloody hell,' and he continued trying to kill Gill with the axe.

Pell had then swiftly moved to the driver's door and from two feet fired twice more through the glass. One bullet missed, and ricocheted around the interior, ending up in a quarter light. The other entered Hughes' left shoulder.

But still Hughes carried on his attack.

Pell was about to shoot for a fourth time when Nicholls came alongside. He thrust the revolver inside the shattered window and fired with the muzzle in contact with Billy's jacket. The bullet went through his back into his heart.

Hughes jerked back mid attack, his arm frozen in the air. He slumped and fell across Gill. She had his blood on her face and was hysterical. The axe fell to the floor.

A wall of police ran forward. Gill put her hand to her face – it was covered in blood. She actually thought her nose had been cut off. All she remembered from the mayhem was hearing someone say 'get her out.'

They dragged her from the car. Her face was bleeding but she was alive. Howse was helped out too, with bloodstains down the side of his beige jacket but no injuries.

The blood of William Thomas Hughes filled the well of the passenger seat. He was seconds from death.

Ambulances whisked Hughes and Gill Moran to Macclesfield General Hospital. She had a minor cut to her face but was in a state of deep shock.

Hughes was pronounced dead on arrival and his body moved to the morgue.

One of the most extraordinary episodes in British legal history was over.

Derbyshire Police Log, Friday January 14th 1977.

11.02pm … 'The woman hostage has been taken from Hughes almost unscathed. C/I Howse did a good job talking to Hughes but he eventually made a move for the girl. Hughes has been taken to hospital. I think he's dead.

Caller : D/I Burgess.

Received by: Comms Room, Buxton.

Means: Telephone.

AFTERMATH

41

The Pottery Cottage murders shocked Britain. People woke up on that Saturday morning unable to comprehend the sheer scale of horror of what they were seeing and hearing on the news.

A criminal with a record of violence had somehow acquired a lethal knife in prison and attacked two warders in a civilian taxi nearly killing one, and seriously wounding another. Then, despite a police manhunt, he'd systematically slaughtered an innocent family in a moorland cottage. The killing spree had ended in a shoot-out with the Derbyshire force firing guns for the first time in history.

It was more like a TV movie than real life.

Outside of his family, there were few people who didn't think he'd got what he'd deserved - bullets to the head and heart. Indeed, an inquest jury would later return a verdict of justifiable homicide.

But the police had a duty to follow procedure like any other crime. Peel and Nichols were required to immediately hand over their guns and ammunition, and a scene of crime team employed full vigour establishing the circumstances of Hughes' death.

After a debrief which lasted into the early hours, Howse slipped quietly away to go back to Derbyshire. Before going off duty he took a detour to Pottery Cottage. He wouldn't be able to sleep without seeing for himself the place on his patch where it all occurred.

News came too late for the national newspapers, but the Sundays ran background articles on Billy Hughes and what reporters had managed to glean about the cottage killings from hastily arranged news conferences organised by the Derbyshire and Cheshire forces.

Above all else, there was massive sympathy for Gill Moran. It was impossible to imagine what she had gone through and the depth of anguish she was now suffering.

Even the coroner, Michael Swanwick, describing it as the most horrible and tragic case he'd ever dealt with, would excuse her from having to attend court.

Gill was put in a private suite away from other patients. Just after midnight, they dressed the wounds on her face and gave her sedatives to get her through the night. A nurse and a WPC stayed at her bedside.

In the morning they gave her more medication. She began to wonder if her ordeal had been real or imagined. She asked the police women what had happened, but they looked away and changed the subject. She kept asking and asking, but they talked about anything rather than what had happened.

In the morning, a young nurse accompanied her to the bathroom and kept an eye on her while she washed, and then held her hand going back to the room.

The police were anxious to formally interview her as soon as was practically possible, but were of course mindful of her mental state.

The medics advised it would be at least another 24 hours before she could hear the terrible truth of what had happened to her family. Radio and TVs were switched off. Newspapers were banned from her floor. Visitors were kept at bay.

The next day, the nurse told her that a superintendent was on his way, but not to be alarmed, he looked more like Father Christmas than a policeman. And he did!

And, standing by the bed with the nurse holding her hand, he told her in hushed tones everything they'd found at Pottery Cottage. It took a while for her to take everything in. The room went silent. She finally spoke. 'So, there's no one left then?' The superintendent squeezed her other hand and quietly replied, 'No love, no one.'

42

TWO days after the shoot-out, Gillian Ann Moran, aged 38, a shorthand typist of Pottery Cottage, Baslow Road, Eastmoor, Chesterfield, began re-living her terror in the form of a police statement.

There were two officers present, a male and a female. They told her to take her time, to stop for a break whenever she wanted, even if it meant taking several sessions and more than one day to complete.

Gill lit a cigarette.

She began by confirming her name, age, occupation and address, and details of her mother, Doris Amy Minton, aged 68, her father, Arthur Minton, aged 72, husband Richard Moran, 41 and daughter Sarah Bridget, ten.

She said their home was an old building that had been modernised. It belonged to her husband and that Richard, herself and Sarah lived in one half and the Mintons in the other.

'We would see Mum and Dad during the daytime but not very often during the evening,' she said.

She explained how at about 8.40am on Wednesday January 12th, 1977 she left home to go to work, dropping Sarah off at her school, Wigley Primary in Old Brampton, on the way. Richard had gone to Birmingham that day on business and they'd left home at roughly the same time.

She said she'd seen her mother before she left but not her father. She had seen him the night before and he was all right then, as was her mother.

Gill continued on how she'd done her normal day's work and left at 3pm. Sarah normally went home on the bus, she said.

When she got home at around 3.15pm she put her car in the garage and went through the back gate which was open. 'This is unusual. We keep it closed because of the dogs.'

The back door was locked. 'This is also unusual, so I knocked. My mother came to the door and opened it. She seemed normal. She said, 'there's a man here with a knife, he's hiding from the police. Keep calm, don't panic and he won't hurt us.'

'I had walked into the kitchen by this time. A man then walked into the kitchen from the hall. I had never seen this man before, and I hadn't heard anything about a prisoner escaping.

'The man said something like, 'I won't hurt you, just do as I say.' He also said he'd escaped from a taxi and the police were after him. He was about 5ft 5ins tall, of slim build, and had a lot of tattoos. He was wearing a blue suit. I don't think he told me his name, but he must have mentioned it to Mum because she was calling him Billy.

'I was quite calm at first. I made a cup of coffee for all of us. We stood in the kitchen and drank it. He sat at the kitchen table and talked about what he had done.

'He said he'd taken over a taxi and taken money from people in the car. I had trouble catching what he said because of his accent and quiet voice.'

Gill explained about the layout of the cottage and how before she'd arrived home the man had already locked all the doors and kept all the keys and cut the telephone wire.

She went through her recollection of Sarah coming home from school; preparing for Richard's arrival; and how they were waiting for darkness to fall so the man could leave.

'Up until this time, his manner was friendly,' she said.

She recalled in methodical detail how the man and Dad mended the phone, then how her friend had called warning of an escaped prisoner – oh, but she'd forgotten to say that when she got home the man had two axes, but she didn't know whose they were.

'He also had a boning knife which he had taken from my father who used to be a grocer. It was years old and very sharp. The man carried it about in the waistband of his trousers and every time he sat down it fell out.'

Gill then relived the terror of that evening – Richard's arrival home, him looking dazed seeing her in the lounge with the knife at her throat; the man tying them all up, her Dad defying him; Sarah getting upset; the intruder gagging them all with cut-up towels; how he'd carried them all upstairs; how Mum had broken free, thinking the man had gone; hearing 'thumps and thuds' from the lounge; the man arriving with tea… and sexually assaulting her.

She told how the next morning, Thursday, she held cups for everyone as they drank their tea and tried to comfort them. All except Sarah. 'I didn't know where Sarah was, I never saw her again.'

She'd seen Dad on a chair in the lounge, covered up as far as his neck in something dark. 'He wasn't moving, I knew he was dead.' But she couldn't bring herself to actually believe what she'd seen with her own eyes.

Gill's statement ran to 29 pages. Hour by hour, sometimes minute by minute, Gill managed an almost forensic account of her nightmare – not being allowed to see Dad or Sarah; how the man kept taking food and drink through to them; playing cards with their captor; and her horror at seeing her mother stagger out of the cottage with her throat cut.

The officers were the first to hear the full facts of what happened in that cottage. They raised their eyebrows hearing how at least four times the Morans had spurned the chance to raise the alarm.

But they were there to take an evidential statement, not to pass judgement one way or the other.

Gill said in her statement that fear had stopped them contacting the police – fear of what he might do to their family; fear that any police intervention might go wrong; and how all the while they thought that he would be leaving in the next hour.

43

After several days under sedation, she was allowed to leave hospital. She went to live with her close friends Grenville and Linda Browett in their little stone cottage not far from Pottery Cottage.

The couple proved absolute rocks of care, loyalty and love. They impressed upon her that instead of being a guest in their home, they'd now expanded into a family of three. Grenville told her they were now brother and sister.

Only the previous weekend, the two couples had enjoyed a dinner party. It was all jolly, friendly, wining and dining and dancing to music. They talked about going on a family holiday together to Brittany.

Now they were planning funerals.

Gill decided she wanted four identical red coffins – she said she couldn't possibly have coped with seeing a little one for Sarah.

On the day, Grenville held her arm as she walked through the door of the church. He felt her body sag as she caught sight of the coffins for the first time.

Someone said at the service that her family were never dead as long as they were in her heart and she took comfort from that. She felt her mother watching over her, willing her not to be destroyed by grief.

The community rallied to support, delivering food and flowers, cigarettes and coffee, doing washing, helping in the house. They worked out a rota so that someone was always with her during those terrible few weeks. Police became friends, local journalists respected Gill's privacy, and were even protective of her.

Step by step she set out on the road to normality – walking the dogs on the Moors, doing simple household tasks, even going back to work. It was of course hard for her colleagues too, wondering what to say and how to say it. But they stood by her and admired her strength and resolve.

***

In the offices of the Daily Mail in Fleet Street the editor David English called an urgent meeting of his senior editorial team.

In pure commercial terms, the story ticked every box of its readership profile. A happy, middle-class family wiped out by a crazed knifeman, the product of a liberal society that had gone soft on crime.

English wanted to go big, blow rival publications out of the water. He sought boardroom approval for the paper's biggest-ever venture into chequebook journalism.

They agreed to pay Gill Moran more than £25,000 – the equivalent of more than £150,000 today - for the exclusive rights to her story and the use of family photographs. An approach was made via the police and to Gill's family solicitor.

Friends encouraged her to accept the offer. It was a lot of money, the foundations to rebuild her life. Left unsaid was the fact that she could never go back to live at Pottery Cottage which would now have to be sold. And given its notoriety, the price would be reduced considerably.

Gill agreed, and two weeks after the tragedy, the Mail sent one of Fleet Street's finest writers, Lynda Lee-Potter, to Derbyshire.

Lee-Potter visited Pottery Cottage – now emptied and cleansed. She told friends she had no doubt that wickedness had left its mark on the bricks and mortar and seeped into the woodwork. She said she felt terrified. She could feel a tangible, all-pervasive feeling of malevolence and evil.

She stayed in the plush Cavendish Hotel on the fringe of the Chatsworth Estate and not far from Pottery Cottage. She stayed for a week, but slept every night with the lights on.

Mrs Moran proved a willing and extraordinary interviewee. Under the headline 'THE MURDERS AT POTTERY COTTAGE,' The Mail ran the story over ten days, a day-by-day account of Gill's nightmare, running alongside family and scene of crime pictures.

The series culminated in a sit-down interview and a hard-hitting opinion piece written by one of the paper's senior editors, highlighting 'shameful errors' in the whole episode.

Lee-Potter proved a sensitive, observant and professional writer. She described the first time she met Gill.

'She was sitting on the sofa in the old, safe, pretty cottage where she lives today.

'Her hands were icily cold, she was wearing black trousers, a white polo-necked sweater; slight and frail with the wide, soft mouth, the sweet diffident smile.'

'Horror and grief annihilated her and she wept compulsively with her arms tightly wrapped around her body, swaying backwards and forwards.

'Grenville came in and knelt down in front of her, putting his arms around her as though she were a child, leaning his forehead against hers, rocking her to and fro and very gently stroking her hair.'

Gill told Lee-Potter: 'In the beginning, people would be in the room, talking and I'd look at them and I could hear the sounds but didn't know what they were saying.

'I try so hard. Some days I get up with so much anger inside me and I think "I won't be beaten, I won't."

'I know that Mum and Dad and Richard and Sarah are watching me, willing me somehow to be able to go on. I believed in God – still believe in God – but why me, why leave me, why take Sarah?

'I always used to say: "I don't know how I can stand it when anything happens to Mum and Dad", but they had a life.

'Sarah was growing into such a lovely girl, and Richard, it was all happening for him. It was right at the beginning of the good times for Richard. He tried so hard for us and Oh I did want him to be proud of me.

'Some days I want to think about Richard and Sarah, but I can't. I daren't. If I let them into my mind I'd go mad. I have to black them out sometimes just so that I can get through the day.

'Some days I just want to go upstairs and scream and pull my hair. I've so much hate in my heart for Hughes and before I'd never hated anybody in my life. Thank God, thank God he's dead. If he'd been alive he'd haunt me forever.'

Lee-Potter wrote of Gill's patience, her pride, her guts, her angry determination not to go under; her fear of becoming dependent on sleeping pills, and how after all that she'd gone through how she displayed little self-pity, and remarkably little bitterness.

'The rare, shallow ones on the fringes of her close-knit circle say: 'My God, she's marvellous, isn't it amazing she's getting over it.'

'She ISN'T getting over it, she's getting on with it. They haven't seen the almost superhuman strength, the way she catches her breath when grief threatens to destroy her. The pride that makes her wear waterproof mascara, her gritty resoluteness to do the only thing she can do now for her family and that is to survive as a complete person.'

'She doesn't want people to be careful. She doesn't want them to be continuously monitoring every word in case it upsets her, because life isn't like that.

'The only way she can cope is for people to act normally, to occasionally cause her terrible, sudden involuntary heartache.

'She knows it's inevitable. She's made the superhuman effort and gone back to work. She doesn't want to be cosseted and protected and removed from reality.'

Just before publication of her story, to escape public attention Gill flew by private jet to France to stay with her sister Barbara who lived in Paris.

44

In the aftermath of the moors murders the question on the nation's lips was 'Why?'

Everyone had a view – even the vicar who presided over the funeral of the victims.

Canon C. Stanley Branson said 'do-gooders' had failed Hughes in his childhood. In the parish magazine, he singled out the influences that had shaped Hughes into a killer – he cited his parents who had failed to correct him as a child; the teachers who failed to teach moral principles; the 'soft-hearted' magistrates giving inadequate punishment for early offences.

'Any or all of these things combined to lead up to the final horror and ended only when police had the courage to act as they did by the roadside in Cheshire,' he said.

There were attempts to politicise the killings too.

A Conservative candidate Edward Oliver said, 'All of us are to a degree responsible since we are part of a society which by its permissive attitudes brought this affair into being. Now is the time surely to ask where the 'wishy-washy' permissive attitudes of our social reformers are leading us. The men of violence do not respect the views of our current society; they scorn them as signs of weakness.'

The local paper, the Derbyshire Times, published a list of key questions that needed answering.

WHY was Hughes, known to the prison authorities as a violent criminal, allowed out of jail without a thorough body search?

WHY in transit was he not manacled in such a way that it would have been impossible for him to overpower two warders?

WHY wasn't a full-scale search made of the prison following the loss of a seven-inch knife which disappeared five weeks before he escaped?

WHY was the police hunt mounted in such a way that Hughes was able to cross an open snow-covered moor and take a family hostage?

WHY was the search from the crash point not concentrated more on the section wide-open for the escape?

WHY were some premises visited many times by police and others completely avoided?

There was anger too. Local people in Chesterfield prevented Hughes being buried there by filling in the grave with their bare hands. Relatives said they didn't want their loved ones resting beside a mass murderer.

One of the protestors, Doreen Vickers, whose brother-in-law was buried there, was related to Hughes' girlfriend Tess and had even entertained him in her home. The day after the protest she received a death threat with a Blackpool postmark.

In the end, at the behest of his estranged wife Jean, Hughes was cremated and his ashes scattered in the grounds of a Roman Catholic church in Blackpool.

Tess, who'd gone out with Hughes for ten months, was at the receiving end of threats too because of her association with Hughes. There was malicious gossip that the papers had offered her £30k for her story.

She said she'd put her own life at risk immediately after his escape by going to their usual haunts with undercover-police protection hoping to flush Hughes out.

'Yes I was offered money, but if anyone needs money it's Mrs Moran, not me. I can manage on my dole money. I don't need no-one else's money. I don't need blood money. I just wish to God it would have been me and not that family. I really mean that.'

Tess was forced out of town by what she called 'wagging tongues and dirty looks,' saying that people were blaming her for bringing Hughes to Chesterfield in the first place. She went to live in a secret address in Leeds to rebuild her life.

A friend said, 'She began believing that she was almost responsible for what happened to that family. She turned into a nervous wreck just thinking about it even though Hughes was now dead.'

In Parliament there were demands for an independent public inquiry into the whole Pottery Cottage affair.

The Opposition Conservative Home Affairs spokesman William Whitelaw called it 'one of the most serious breakdowns in security arrangements affecting the police, public and prison service since the last war.'

'There is deep and widespread concern about the handling of the case. I have received very disturbing reports from responsible people in the area concerned.'

He was backed by the fiery local Labour MP Tom Swain, a former miner and fairground boxer, who said the sensation should not be allowed to die in a couple of days.

'The truth should be known to everybody,' he said.

The Home Secretary said he was waiting for a report from the Chief Constable of Derbyshire before deciding. But he had ordered an immediate inquiry into security at Leicester to be carried out by the Chief Inspector of Prisons.

In his office at Ripley HQ, the Assistant Chief Constable Mitchell drew up a report for his boss – one that he knew would eventually go to the very top.

Since bobbies first walked the beat there in 1857, Derbyshire was always considered one of the safest counties in the country with huge swathes of countryside, market towns and only one big conurbation, the city of Derby. Up until the killing of Hughes, firearms had never been used by the Force.

In his report Mitchell made clear that if the officers had not fired at Hughes, then Mrs Moran would have been killed. Immediately after the incident he'd gone to Pottery Cottage to supervise the investigation.

'Mrs Minton was found covered in snow in the corner of the garden. There were obvious signs that the body had been dragged there from near the front drive.'

In the downstairs lounge was the body of Arthur Minton. His hands were tied behind his back. He was lying in the corner near the alcove in a position that he could not be seen from the hallway inside the house, nor from the window facing onto the back yard.

On the landing upstairs was the body of Richard Moran. His feet were tied.

In the rear of the second part of the house was the body of Sarah Bridget Moran, aged ten. Her feet and wrists were tied and she was lying on the floor in the corner of the room.

'Dr Alan Usher, a Home Office pathologist, attended and examined the bodies in situ. All appeared to have stab wounds to the neck and body, the neck wounds in each case being very severe.

'A full scientific examination was made of the house and 17 fingerprints were found, identical to those of the prisoner Hughes.'

He stated that two weeks after the murders, 130 officers carried out a full-scale search across the snow-covered moors in the general direction it now seemed probable was the route taken by Hughes.

They found prison papers taken by him from the hi-jacked taxi. The stolen prison knife was eventually found in a field by the side of Pottery Cottage, about 300 yards on the Baslow side of the house, near to the wall adjoining the main road.

As the crow flies, the distance between the crashed taxi and the cottage was roughly two and a half miles, but he must have walked a great deal further, said Mitchell.

'From Mrs Moran's statement that she heard no noises from the part of the cottage occupied by Mr and Mrs Minton, nor from the lounge of her own part of the house, after Wednesday evening, it seems probable that Hughes killed the difficult Mr Minton and the child on the Wednesday night. It will be recalled that Mr Minton was somewhat troublesome to Hughes and the child was, possibly, showing more pluck than her parents.

'Hughes made life appear quite normal at the Moran household and Mr and Mrs Moran, by their willing co-operation, enabled him to do this.

'Both Mr and Mrs Moran had several opportunities to escape and give warning without there being any further danger to their family, but for some reason they chose not to avail themselves of their chances.

'Whatever happened at the house did not cause the slightest suspicion to anybody in the neighbourhood.

'I have examined all details of the police search for Hughes between Wednesday morning and Friday evening. There was intelligence and information which indicated that he was making towards Preston in Lancashire and therefore, a very reasonable assumption that he would do just this.

'The other main possibility was that he would seek shelter in Chesterfield and the appropriate action was taken for both of these circumstances.

'There was nothing to suggest that he had gone up hill in the direction of Eastmoor and when looking at the terrain between the abandoned car and Pottery Cottage, it appeared a most unlikely and difficult route for any person to take. Shelter and cover were more readily available in the westerly direction.

He said during the whole three days there was nothing whatsoever arising from discussions which indicated that his assessment at the time was wrong.

There was a clamour for the police report to be made public but it would remain confidential for more than 40 years, obtained by the author of this book, after an application under the Freedom of Information Act.

45

Amid the welter of recrimination over the Hughes escape and subsequent killing spree, it was perhaps the Prison Service that came under the most scrutiny. The crimes had opened up the debate about the whole purpose of prison. Was it to punish or rehabilitate? And was the prison regime somehow to blame for creating the monster that was William Thomas Hughes?

Most people's perception of prison life was gleaned from the popular BBC Sitcom Porridge, watched by millions every week. Comedian/actor Ronnie Barker played a cheeky-chappie habitual thief called Fletcher who enjoyed harmless daily battles with the strict disciplinarian screw Mckay.

That fictional portrayal of doing bird couldn't have been further from the truth. Prisons in the seventies were no laughing matter.

Britain had just witnessed its worst jail riot in nearly half a century. Nearly 200 prisoners had staged a three-day rooftop protest at Hull against brutality by staff.

Damage ran into millions of pounds, and the prison needed to close for a year. In all, 185 prisoners were charged with a total of 523 breaches of prison rules.

The riot shocked Britain, opening up the debate about penal policy.

Academics argued that such institutions had become breeding grounds of more crime and an ineffective as a way of rehabilitation.

They pointed to a study that revealed of the men discharged from corrective training, more than 60 per cent had been reconvicted within a year – many of those whilst under supervisory after-care.

This against a background of a financial and political crisis, with the economy in deep recession forcing cuts in public services.

There'd been strikes and power blackouts; inflation was running at over 20 per cent; interest rates were sky high; more than a million people were out of work, and government borrowing had spiralled out of control.

Worse was to come. The new Labour Prime Minister James Callaghan was about to go begging to the International Monetary Fund for 'bailout' loans running into billions of pounds.

In return, the IMF would insist on further severe cuts in public spending, impacting hugely on social provision, including the prison service.

It was a vicious downward spiral. More unemployment led to more crime. More crime meant more arrests. More arrests caused a huge backlog of cases, meaning more remand prisoners, living two or three in cells designed for one.

When cases were eventually heard, more convictions meant more prisoners flooding already overstretched and overcrowded institutions.

Hardliner politicians pointed the finger at the prison service itself. Instead of being a deterrent, prisons had become holiday camps, they said.

Politicians sensed popular support. The wave of IRA bombs in Northern Ireland had spread to mainland Britain.

The public mood was for revenge on terrorists and a tougher line on criminals. They demanded – and got - longer sentences, restrictions to parole, and an end to supposed mollycoddling of inmates.

Prison governors were a certain breed. Dedicated, resilient, driven by a duty to public service. Anonymous. Some came up through the ranks - former prison officers who knew the score, and the intimate workings of the system. Others were parachuted-in by the civil service as a reward for their political nous and management skills.

They kept a low-profile. They were encouraged to steer clear of any media. You wouldn't see a picture of a prison governor handing over a cheque in the local paper, writing articles in the national press about prison policy, or engaging in network TV debate. Governors were expected to quietly toe the hard line or make way for someone who would.

Word came down from the Home Office that staff must be tough, and to adopt a no-nonsense approach to prison discipline. There were reductions in exercise, visiting rights, association, and recreational facilities.

Many screws felt they were employed not just to guard villains, but had a duty to the Crown to punish them. Unsanctioned beatings were common, particularly at night, when punishment squads took off their hobnailed boots, put on slippers, and crept along the landings to ambush prisoners in their cells.

There were complaints of violence, bribery, withholding letters, and trumped-up charges. But an inmate could never win. Governors ALWAYS backed their men. Many cons who demanded a hearing were fined for making 'frivolous' complaints.

The service employed many ex-squaddies as screws. Some had witnessed their buddies blown to pieces by terrorist bombs. In Northern Ireland internment had stripped prisoners of their normal rights and screws across England saw themselves as society's enforcers.

Recruitment was handled centrally. 'Essential qualities' were listed as humanity, firmness, maturity, patience, understanding, leadership and a sense of humour. The reality was that if you were reasonably fit and could breathe, you could become a prison officer.

The basic requirement was you had to be British, aged between 22 and 44 years, at least 5ft tall, and be in good health. You didn't need any exam qualifications. Candidates were required to take four short very simple written tests that would barely tax a ten-year-old.

A typical question was 'underline the correct word – he {flewed/flied/flew} to America as this was quicker {than/from/in} going by sea.'

'Fill in the missing number represented by the asterisks – 3,6,9,12,15, **, 21.'

Things had become so bad in jails up and down the country that a group of ex-cons formed a prisoners' rights organisation (PROP) who organised more that 100 prison demonstrations, strikes and protests.

Its aim was not just to protect rights, but to assist in prisoners' rehabilitation and re-integration into society 'so as to bring about a reduction in crime.'

It organised a 24-hour general strike involving 10,000 prisoners – a quarter of the prison population – across 33 prisons, including Leicester.

While repairs were taking place at Hull, the authorities had the task of rehousing every inmate, including using Leicester, creating an even bigger overcrowding headache for the management there.

Under pressure from the media and public, The Home Secretary ordered an inquiry into the Hughes escape. But its brief was narrow – to examine Security at Leicester, and the arrangements for conducting prisoners to courts, with particular reference to the escape of Hughes –

thus avoiding the wider issues about the direction of the British Penal System.

It was to be carried out by the Chief Inspector of Prisons, Gordon Fowler. He had already carried out an Inquiry into the Hull riot. Now he was heading for Leicester.

Even as he started work, nearly 200 prison officers at Leicester began industrial action in a bid to force an independent inquiry into the circumstances leading to the knife attack on two of their colleagues. They feared a cover-up and refused to escort prisoners to court and would not co-operate over visits to the jail by solicitors.

'We want the public to know all the facts and we want no whitewash,' said a union official.

46

On March 9th 1977 - two months after Pottery Cottage - Fowler presented his report to the Home Secretary.

He'd interviewed 45 witnesses and had every co-operation from the governor and his staff, he said.

His report offered a damning insight into the workings of a typical jail. For the first time it highlighted the failures inside Leicester and revealed how Hughes had acquired the knife.

Over the years Leicester Prison – built in 1825 – had housed some of the country's most notorious criminals. Only one man had ever escaped. And he'd broken his ankle landing in the governor's garden from a smaller, internal wall.

It had celebrated its opening with a triple public execution outside the main entrance. Three men were hanged for horse stealing. Thousands of people turned up, half of them women and children, a day out for all, with street sellers and a fairground atmosphere.

Fowler found a prison bursting at the seams. The certified normal accommodation of cells was 218, but the occupation of prisoners averaged 368, about a third of those sleeping three to a cell.

The pressure-cooker atmosphere had led to assaults on staff, rumours of disturbance or demonstration, the testing out of staff by use of insolence, and concerted questioning of rights and privileges by the inmates.

And it wasn't just the prisoners complaining. The governor had been forced by budget cuts to reduce staff and insist wardens work longer hours.

And, of the 100 officers at Leicester, sixty per cent had less than five years experience. There was a real shortage of workshop instructors in particular.

The staff union, the Prison Officers' Association, had raised a number of grievances – under-manning; the loss of cuff keys and security keys; and weaknesses in communication which they said contributed to security defects.

They'd formally complained that the governor had a preoccupation with the special wing, housing IRA terrorists, the Kray gangster twins, and some of the great train robbers. All this to the detriment of the main 'bread and butter' inmates, they claimed.

The admin of most nicks was akin to the running of department stores – autonomous empires reporting to an MD, or in this case, the governor.

For example, the Discipline Office, responsible for the computation of dates and release, and acting as the handmaiden of the court, was a separate entity from the Security Department, which monitored the intelligence of the prison as a whole, searched for clandestine material, and liaised with the police on high-security prisoners.

It was the same for the Regulating Office, whose main task was the provision and detail of escort staff.

Liaison and communication between departments was poor, through a mix of incompetence and low staffing levels. Messages went unheeded, papers were misplaced or lost, and vital intelligence not passed on.

There was a feeling the right hand didn't always know what the left hand was doing, and the system suffered from one-upmanship and petty jealousy.

Police had warned on the official admission form 293 that Hughes was a prisoner who presented a special risk – of escape, suicide and violence. The form was received in the Discipline Office the day after Hughes arrived. But it was no more than a tickbox exercise, with no explanation on the form as to why police had come to that conclusion and nothing was done.

The form was made available to the Reception Board, whose role it was to assist in his integration into the prison system, but they paid no heed. Hughes told them he was not guilty of the alleged rape and wanted to buckle down whilst on remand and concentrate on proving his innocence.

The form was not sent to the Security Department, nor added to the prisoner's record.

It was a similar story in the Observation and Classification Unit, concerned with the categorisation of prisoners, the allocation of work, and the preparation of parole documents.

It was its responsibility to assess his security risk and to report its findings to the prison governor. It operated under criteria laid down by the Home Office who had drawn up four categories of risk.

Category A was for those whose escape would be highly dangerous to the public, police or the security of the state;

Category B for whom the very highest conditions of security were not necessary, but for whom escape must be made very difficult;

Category C was for "low-risk" potential escapees; whilst Category D was for those inmates who could be reasonably trusted to serve their time in open conditions.

Assessing him as Cat A, would have entailed a submission to Prison Department Headquarters in Whitehall with supporting documents.

Guarding highly dangerous prisoners was far more costly than other inmates, with implications for extra staffing, accommodation and added security, particularly ferrying terrorists and murderers to court.

A major factor was the nature of the charge against him. Such a submission should have been made if he was charged with a sexual assault involving the use of violence. However, the wording on the charge sheet before the Classification Unit was incomplete – 'having sexual intercourse with a woman without her consent,' which did not convey the impression of violence.

Regarding the male victim, an update to the more serious charge of grievous bodily harm with intent was never forwarded.

No one in the jail had the full updated version of Hughes' criminal record. That was still in an office somewhere at Prison HQ.

The Classification Unit had relied on his assurances that he'd be a good prisoner and would be no trouble to anyone and duly classified him as Category B. It meant a dangerous prisoner was officially deemed, 'run-of-the-mill.'

As one of the injured prison officers, Donald Sprintall, said after leaving hospital, 'We'd no reason to suspect he was dangerous. As far as we knew he was just an ordinary remand prisoner to be handed over to the police at a magistrates court.

'If we'd known he was of a violent nature he would have been searched more thoroughly and been given a strip search. The powers-that-be would have probably decided he would go under a security escort.'

194

There had never been a desire, or indeed resource, to examine or investigate any concerns over his mental state. And he was put to work in the kitchen.

Adding to this 'run of the mill' impression was the number of times Hughes appeared in court on remand. He was playing a canny game of delay and obfuscation to put off Judgement Day. In all he appeared at Chesterfield NINE times on the same charges.

The way the system worked was that Committal hearings were required to be before Magistrates who, after hearing the evidence, had to decide if there was a case to answer before a judge and a jury at a Crown Court.

But these proceedings were a costly and cumbersome business, and open to abuse by the defence, particularly where a witness was also a victim.

Hughes engineered adjournment after adjournment; delay after delay; witnesses not available; legal team not briefed; papers not ready; summonses not served.

On Nov 18th papers were served on his solicitors in Blackpool and Chesterfield, acting as agents, that committal proceedings were planned for the 26th November.

However the day before that next hearing, his Blackpool solicitors phoned the police stating they would be asking for an adjournment. A week later, at another hearing, his Chesterfield solicitors said they'd received no instructions from Blackpool.

On 10th December he'd refused a Section 1 Committal, stating that he wanted the woman in the case to give evidence.

On the 17th he said that he had second thoughts and it wouldn't be necessary to put the woman and her boyfriend through the ordeal of a public court appearance. But after they'd gone home, he changed his mind, insisting they appear, meaning yet another postponement.

On Christmas Eve, he'd appeared again and a full committal was arranged for the 11th January. But later that day, when most people were thinking of Christmas, his Chesterfield team phoned the court stating that Hughes would revert to a Section 1 on his next routine weekly appearance on Jan 5th.

But when he appeared on the 5th he again changed his mind and the case was adjourned for the umpteenth time until January 12th 1977, the day he escaped.

All this time Hughes was employed in the kitchen and was said to have worked well in a demanding job. He was described by the kitchen staff as 'not out of the ordinary.' His relationship with other prisoners was said to be 'nothing outstanding.'

He played games with them during recreational periods and he was not a loner. He was chatty with the senior officer Caterer and had at one point complained he'd been stitched up by the system.

His behaviour was always satisfactory and there were no reports of misconduct. He earned the full one-third remission of sentence.

Fowler revealed that just before 9am a month before his escape, a seven-inch boning knife, used to cut meat from joints in the preparation of sandwiches, had gone missing in the kitchen where Hughes worked.

As was procedure, the prison's security department was informed, and arrangements made to search the kitchens from top to bottom, including the cells of the prisoners employed there. Two officers were even deployed to the refuse skip. They spent an hour going through tons of rotting food and packaging.

The staff had gone through the list of inmates who'd had access to the sandwich-making area. Hughes had been up early that day working with the knife, making sandwiches. He'd been collected from the kitchen by one of the two escorting officers and taken to reception where he changed from his prison clothes into his civilian suit to attend court.

The Principal Officer (Security) was instructed by the prison's Regulation Officer to 'intercept the escort' on the way to Chesterfield and he instructed the escort team to search and question Hughes about the knife.

There were three other prisoners involved in the escort, all remands, two for Chesterfield Magistrates Court, the other for Burton on Trent. Two of the remands were handcuffed together and the other remand handcuffed to Hughes, both sitting in the front seat of the minibus.

196

There was no phone or radio contact with the vehicle, so after arriving at the courthouse, a message was passed to the escorting officers to phone Leicester prison urgently. They got through to the security officer with instructions to search him immediately.

Hughes was in the courthouse cell waiting to appear when the officers burst in. They gave him a 'rub-down' and searched the cell but found nothing. 'I don't know what you're on about,' he'd told them.

Back at the prison, the loss of the knife was soon forgotten. Fowler examined all the records but found just one entry – in the security officer's diary – which read '3 Dec 1976. Knife reported missing in the kitchen. Extensive search made of kitchen and surrounding area but to no avail.'

Outside of that, the incident wasn't recorded, no follow-ups or statements taken, nor staff as a whole informed and certainly not the governor. No mention of the theft, or details of the search were ever added to his prison record, and Hughes returned to the same cell to continue his sentence.

'The search was not co-ordinated or pursued with sufficient vigour. Most of the staff interviewed during the course of my Inquiry were indeed unaware that a knife was missing until after the escape four weeks later,' reported Fowler.

But not everyone was satisfied. The catering officer who first reported the knife missing felt that the search should have been intensified and that Hughes should have become the subject of special security surveillance.

He even phoned his boss, who was off sick, twice that afternoon to express his concern. He was told that he'd done his bit by reporting the incident and that security 'had it in hand.' In short, the whole incident had been swept under the carpet.

Fowler officially reported 'a failure by management and staff to pursue with sufficient vigour the search for the missing knife.' Standard searching procedures were not followed and no records kept of any searches made by staff.

He found weaknesses in communications at different levels.

However he was adamant that the information received by the prison authorities from the police was insufficient to identify Hughes as a person prone to extreme violence or as a potentially dangerous psychopath.

'The escape on 12 January 1977, and its tragic consequences, must compel a review of the way in which routine information is conveyed.

'Standard forms themselves become routinised and tend to lose their effect where questions of security arise; and in this case the routine information contained in the police form was not supplemented in any way.'

Fowler also recommended that strip-searches be introduced for all prisoners passing through reception rather than 'rub-down' searches.

'A rub-down' search if properly carried out will detect most clandestine objects but is not 100 per cent effective. In Hughes case the rub-down searches appear to have been variable in quality.'

The Home Secretary said in the Commons he accepted all 17 of Fowler's recommendations of immediate measures to tighten up rules relating to documentation, searching and escorts. But introducing strip searches would require further resources and investigation.

47

Three months after the Pottery Cottage murders, a greying figure in a smart suit met an attractive woman in a clandestine meeting in a pub near the Chatsworth Estate. They ordered soft drinks and chatted quietly and formally about everything but the event that united them – the tragedy of Pottery Cottage.

The woman was Gill Moran, gradually coming to terms with the loss of her family. Her companion was Peter Howse, the police officer who saved her from almost certain death on that wintry night in Cheshire.

The meeting was orchestrated by Gill. She wanted to say thank you to her saviour, even though seeing him in the flesh again brought back painful memories.

Howse noted that she had lost weight. He didn't quite know what to say. He was just doing his duty, he said.

In her Mail interview, she recalled the voice who patiently tried to negotiate with Hughes for nearly an hour – the man who'd dived into the car to put himself between a flying axe and her body.

Lee-Potter wrote that it sounded so firm, so relaxing and assuring, that it lapped over her like warm and gentle seawater on a tropical beach.

Gill was quoted as saying, 'I have never heard such a wonderful voice in the whole of my life and I will never forget it as long as I live. It had such kindness to it, such gentleness, and comfort.'

Their pub rendezvous lasted ten minutes or so before they politely shook hands and went their separate ways.

Howse was to serve 34 years in the police force, rising to the rank of Deputy Chief Constable of Norfolk before retiring in 1992. He was awarded the Queen's Commendation for Bravery and the Queen's Police Medal for Distinguished Service.

For many years he shunned requests for interviews about his part in the episode.

'Looking back, many factors contributed to the ordeal ending the way it did. A healthy portion of luck combined with good judgement meant that the criminal died – and the hostage survived but I've always wondered what might have happened if it had gone the other way,' he told Johnston Press.

'I wonder if I would have got the same support if Gill had died. It's a thin line between success and failure.'

The Pottery Cottage murders had a huge impact on everyone involved. Some of the officers in the case suffered trauma and endured sleepless nights thinking about some of the dreadful images they'd witnessed.

Alan Nicholls, who fired the bullet that killed Hughes, was the first officer in Derbyshire ever to shoot someone dead. He was 50 at the time.

He died in 2009 refusing to ever talk publicly about his role. In 2017, he was given a posthumous bravery award by the Police Federation, the police officers' trade union.

Accepting the honour, his son Simon said, 'Dad was not the sort of person to boast or shout about what he had done. He was a very proud officer who got on with the job.

'When he got home that night he said to my Mum 'I have shot the bugger dead.' But he just saw it as part of his job.'

His other son Roger said that a week after Hughes' death, an officer from Scotland Yard had written in a publication that whoever had shot Hughes would have that on his conscience for the rest of his life.

'But Dad was adamant and said it had to be done.'

Billy's widow Jean Hughes sadly took her own life in 1998. She was found at her home in Blackpool with a plastic bag over her head after taking an overdose.

Everyone hoped and prayed that Gill would enjoy everlasting peace and happiness. She thought she'd found it in the shape of Richard's cousin, Jim Mulqueen, who comforted her after the deaths of her family.

In December 1978 – nearly two years on – they married and settled in Derbyshire. A year later Gill gave birth to a daughter, whom they poignantly named Jayne Sarah.

The proud parents posed for photographs for the media in their home, but the joy wasn't to last.

Eleven years after the events at Pottery Cottage he was jailed for two years for threatening someone with a shotgun.

There'd been a row in a pub in Darley Dale and Mulqueen had rushed home to the cottage he shared with Gill in Matlock to fetch the gun.

When police arrived to arrest him, they were confronted around the back by Mulqueen waving a double-barrelled shotgun at them. Det Sgt Len Haywood managed to talk him down, but he threw the gun in the air and ran off. It landed close to Gill who was standing at the back door. He was arrested by DC Philbin. At the trial, both officers were commended.

After his sentence Gill moved permanently to France to live near her sister where she remains to this day.

In the summer of 2019 it was announced that Peter Howse was writing his own version of the Pottery Cottage murders and that Gill Moran had given her blessing.

48

The Daily Mail cited 'inexcusable and inexplicable incompetence' by the police and prison authorities. But it also asked questions of the Moran family.

'Why did they throw away so many chances? How is it that decent, respectable people could be so dominated by a vicious psychopath like Hughes?' the paper asked.

Chance one came at dawn on Thursday with the arrival of the council sanitation team.

Chance two was later that morning, when Gill was allowed to drive into town to buy newspapers.

Chance three came on the next morning when Richard and Gill went shopping together.

Chance four was when Hughes and the Morans drove to his factory where the all-male nightshift were working. Richard spoke to the factory supervisor but did not mention that they had been taken hostage by an escaped prisoner.

That night too, the couple had the chance to overpower him when he fell into a stupor, but they decided against it.

The clue to their actions might be found in the contrasting personalities of everyone involved.

The murders triggered debate about Hughes' state of mind. His brother David, who along with his mother had gone into hiding after the killings, said that Billy was terrified of facing a long sentence and had a mental breakdown. His marriage had ended and his girlfriend had dumped him, he said.

But how could a human being be so wickedly callous? To attack unarmed men with a knife, tie up an old man and child, slit their throats, and do the same to Amy and Richard?

Hughes was branded a psychopath, a description often bandied about to describe anyone who commits violence or murder. But there was no doubt Hughes fitted that billing.

The Mayo Clinic in America describes psychopathy as a personality disorder where the person typically has no regard for right or wrong. Psychopaths make up roughly one per cent of the general population.

In the seventies, Canadian psychologist, Robert Hare, published a list of 20 personality traits common in psychopaths.

These included pathological lying; portraying glib and superficial charm; a grandiose sense of self, the need for stimulation; cunning and manipulative behaviour; a lack of remorse or guilt; shallow emotional response; callousness and lack of empathy.

They were also sexually promiscuous; displayed early behaviour problems; had a lack of realistic long-term goals; were impulsive; irresponsible; had been in short-term marital relationships; were juvenile delinquents and had shown criminal versatility.

Hughes ticked every box. He displayed every characteristic - highly impulsive and highly emotional.

He revelled in the power of violence and actually got a buzz out of the suffering of his victims. It made him feel important, a big shot.

A trait amongst the most extreme psychopaths like Hughes was to use up-close-and-personal methods to kill – strangulation, bludgeoning and in this case, stabbing. The last thing someone like him would want was to distance himself. The thrill is the torture of the victim, hearing them scream. Pleading and begging for mercy would have made him feel good. The actual killing is a mere footnote.

His main weapons were fear and violence, coupled with an emotional stranglehold of promising that he'd soon be out of the way. He knew that uncertainty about his departures and returns would unnerve his prisoners and increase his hold over them. He knew instinctively when to ramp up the pressure to make them do exactly as ordered.

It's believed that psychopathy has roots in early childhood. Children who show an early lack of fear, indifference towards peers, and appear callous in the face of emotion, are at the greatest risk.

Professor Stephen Scott, from the Institute of Psychiatry at Kings College, London, told the BBC in 2017 that around one in a hundred children displayed psychopathic traits – callous-unemotional acts. Extreme cases would become criminal psychopaths in later life.

They could be superficially charming, but when they saw people in distress they didn't care. They felt no guilt or remorse, were punishment insensitive, and had a short temper, doing something nice for you for five minutes, but it wouldn't last long and if you crossed them they would lose it very quickly and get angry.

Hughes had grown up a street fighter. His dad was in the Army and the family followed him around various postings home and abroad. It meant the young Billy had to fight his way in at new schools to be accepted.

At Pottery Cottage, he told Richard that he never felt pain, not from fights with the other kids, his dad's belt, nor from beatings from screws or coppers.

He recognised his condition. Whilst on remand in Leicester he asked a psychiatrist if he could have the aggressive part of his brain cut out.

. Forty years later that notion wasn't as daft as it might have sounded back then. Psychopathy is a mental disorder. Its cause is primarily biological. Brain scans reveal an area called the amygdala - where humans acknowledge emotions and process them - is completely quiet and flat in some psychopaths.

In purely psychological terms, the Morans were meat and drink for his ratlike cunning. Hughes was a man of violence, Richard a man of peace. His friend Grenville Browett said, 'He detested violence. He was the sort who would try to reason with this man. He never spoke ill of anyone.'

Hughes was an idler who'd hardly done a day's work in his life. Richard on the other hand was a forceful and dynamic man, a man who would work 20 hours a day, a man who was the life and wit of any dinner party.

There's no doubt Richard wanted to raise the alarm when they went out shopping. But he put his wife's emotional wellbeing above his own feelings.

But there was something more that might explain his action – or lack of it while in the grip of Hughes.

It didn't show often, but occasionally the Celtic gods of fatalism and despair would take over and Richard would have a bad day.

His co-directors noted his fatalism. Sometimes when things went wrong he would shrug his shoulders and say 'what will be, will be.'

His firm's Managing Director, David Brown, discussed this with him over drinks. Richard admitted that he often thought that life was planned out and you couldn't alter it.

Brown was quoted in the Mail feature. 'It was life and death he was really fatalistic about. He used to say that if God Almighty said 'come in number ten, your time is up,' that's it, there was nothing you could do.'

Subscribers to that theory of life could point to umpteen 'chance' happenings that conspired to lead to his murder. If only Hughes hadn't gone to the Jingles disco, if only he hadn't spotted the girl, followed her home, raped her, got arrested, been remanded to Leicester instead of another jail, not worked in the prison kitchen, not stolen a knife, if a search had been carried out properly, if he'd have travelled in a secure vehicle rather than a taxi, not taken a random escape route, not crashed the car where he did, had not fled over the moors, if it hadn't snowed... and so on and so on.

What about Gill Moran? All her life she'd been a passive woman. Not weak, but passive. She knew it herself.

'I'm not very good at giving orders, but I'm very good at carrying them out,' she told Lee-Potter.

She was also very trusting, some would say naïve. As a teenager her friends chided her about believing everything that anyone told her.

She also lacked confidence. She admitted that she'd always been insecure, wanting to be liked, seeking and failing to get reassurance from a doting father, protective mother and a loyal husband.

There are suggestions that the Morans, and Gill in particular had become victims of Stockholm Syndrome, where hostages begin to support their captors and fear law enforcement personnel coming to their rescue.

The syndrome was fresh in everyone's mind because three years previously two machine-gun carrying criminals entered a bank in Sweden and took four hostages – three women and a man - for five days. When they were freed it was clear they'd developed an emotional bond with their captors and actually protected them from the police.

Lynda Lee-Potter speculated that the family were gripped by 'automatic compliance' similar to how millions of Jewish people went passively to their deaths with no resistance against their Nazi persecutors.

'The secret of this condition is that while it is induced and controlled by the application of fear, the victims do not feel fearful all the time,' she wrote.

'The Morans, as they sat in their child's room with a clever and vicious homicidal maniac, even managed to drink whisky and play cards.'

Some police officers thought there must have been other factors at play - even that Gill Moran must have known Billy Hughes beforehand.

More than 40 years on, the public are still looking for an explanation as to why they didn't fight back. Internet gossip has fuelled rumours they were one step further, that Hughes and Gill were lovers.

This author, for one, hopes that such an outlandish notion is completely dispelled by this book.

Would any of us really know for certain how we would react in such circumstances, our home invaded, our family at risk?

The Morans were convinced that if they did not comply with Hughes' every command they would die.

Gill believed with every fibre of her being that the way to protect her family was to do as he said. This tragic misjudgement will live with her for the rest of her life.

In memory of Arthur Minton, Amy Minton, Richard Moran and Sarah Moran.

A MESSSAGE FROM THE AUTHOR

Thank you for purchasing my book. I hope you enjoyed it. Can I ask a favour? Would you be kind enough to post a review on Amazon?

Good, bad or indifferent, it doesn't matter. Reviews are very important for self-publishers such as myself and help bring the book to the attention of new readers.

Just go on the Amazon website in your purchasing country and type in Pottery Cottage book by Alan Hurndall. Just a few lines make all the difference.

Many thanks.

Printed in Great Britain
by Amazon